Introduction to the Dienes Mathematics Programme

It is not the purpose of this book to play down the difficulties of learning the basic elements of mathematics. The problem is to try to define what these basic elements are. In his book *The Elements of Mathematics* (published by Herder and Herder, New York, and distributed in England by McGraw-Hill of Maidenhead), Professor Z. P. Dienes states that science subjects in general have clearly defined basic elements which anyone working within these fields is easily able to explain, understand and identify. This, unfortunately, is not true of mathematics, because although mathematics deals with basic elements in just the same way that the sciences do, these basic elements are not defined in an absolute way.

> We may ask how such an abstract science as mathematics can be taught to children and particularly to young children. Just as we ourselves have abstracted mathematical notions from our environment by working up from concrete terms to abstract, so must we reverse this process in our own minds in order to permit the children to grasp a concept of abstraction. We shall have to *un-abstract* mathematics and turn it into something *real* so that the children themselves can explore the same process from the concrete to the abstract that we had initially thought out. This process is known as *learning*. (From *The Elements of Mathematics*, page 15)

In this book I shall attempt to show some concrete situations which might help in understanding these problems and to illustrate 'games' which children can play to help them to learn these basic ideas of mathematics.

Most emphasis is put on the ideas of arithmetic (and algebra), although quite young children can make profitable enquiries in other fields such as logic, geometry, or probability. They will also learn to perceive mathematical relations in the environment and to apply mathematical models in helping to understand their environment better.

For many years it was thought that children who could count should be ready for such ideas as $2+3 = 5$. If the child is to understand rather than just to learn this as a fact (along with dozens of others), he first will need to find out what sort of things 2, 3, 5 are, that is, answer the question, *What are numbers?* Secondly, the equals sign, and other signs like $<$ in $2 < 5$, give rise to the question, *What is a relation?* Thirdly, there is the $+$ and also $-$, $\times$, $\div$, and so on, with the question, *What is an operation?* This book is written in the belief that there is ample evidence to show that children can deal with these ideas at an early age, if they are presented in suitable ways, and in the hope that they will understand better some of the basic ideas of mathematics. However, we shall not achieve the desired result by simply asking and answering the questions; this must be done by the abstraction of the ideas from a multitude of different concrete situations.

The materials described in the book (and listed below) can be obtained from ESA Creative Learning Limited, Pinnacles, P.O. Box 22, Harlow, Essex.

Dienes Logic Blocks (sold under the name *Logiblocs*)
Logicubes
Dienes Multibase Arithmetic Blocks
People Logic Set

Further details are available from the supplier. Similar materials can be obtained from a number of other firms.

Peter L. Seaborne

Dienes Multibase Arithmetic Blocks (M.A.B.)

This system is frequently referred to from Chapter 10 onwards and is drawn out here for the convenience of the reader.

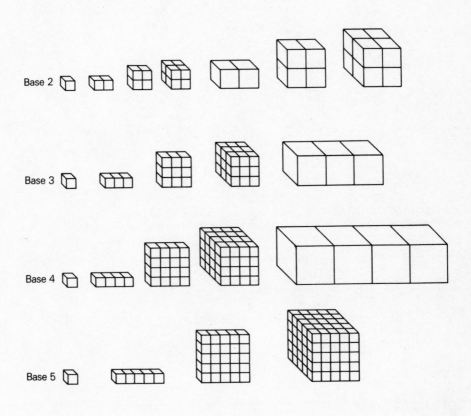

Section I From sets to number

 ## 1   Early Sorting Activities

Introduction

When considering ways of introducing mathematical ideas to young children, we may sensibly decide that among the great variety of experiences which have filled the life of the pre-school child, few have been directly concerned with number. With luck the child may have learned to count, but this has as little to do with arithmetic (and mathematics, in general) as any nursery rhyme and, as far as the child is concerned, probably has rather less meaning. However, these multitudes of experiences contain many seeds of mathematical ideas from which future learning can be developed.

Most people (adults and children alike) seem to learn best by proceeding from the known to the unknown through a range of practical activities. From these activities we distil the abstract ideas which we can subsequently apply to new situations. Unfortunately, it appears to be impossible for a human being to learn such ideas by being told about them; it is thus the teacher's responsibility to present the ideas to the child in situations from which he (the child) can form his own abstractions. It is therefore very important for the teacher really to understand the ideas himself, in order to be able to present a sufficiently wide range of experiences for the child to stand a good chance of making the required abstractions and to organise this information in his mind. Several senses can be used in helping the child to have access to information, these are *kinaesthetic* (the sensation of movement or act of doing something with one's body), *tactile* (the sense of touch and manipulation of objects), *visual*, and *auditory*. Traditional education has tended to rely very heavily on the *auditory* and to a lesser extent on the *visual*, so avoiding the other senses which are probably more sensitive in the young child. The practical considerations of the present-day classroom may result in greater emphasis being placed on tactile rather than·kinaesthetic activity, but the future may see some interesting changes in this state of affairs.

If we are to adopt the pattern of proceeding from the known to the unknown, it is desirable that we should do so from the start. We should not write off the first five years of a child's life as being irrelevant to his education in school, simply because it does not contain what we can readily recognise as formal learning. In fact, the child has lived in an environment richly sown with mathematical seeds. The role of the teacher is to find and nurture them and so bring them to maturity.

The reader may wonder what these seeds might be. They certainly

3

are not shadows of formal arithmetic. As with seeds, it is very difficult to see how they will look when fully developed. Many teachers may need to read the whole of this little book in order to see why the following list includes some of the important seeds.

Every pre-school child will have experience of objects and their properties. It is these properties which enable him to distinguish between objects, and in distinguishing between objects he is considering a variety of relations, for example, 'That car is the same as Daddy's', 'Your piece of cake is bigger than mine', 'All those bricks go in this box.' The child's knowledge of the properties of objects (even if he cannot verbalise his ideas) will enable him to sort and classify, thus putting his objects into sets—'These are my sweets, yours are over there!' Most children are beginning to be aware of one-to-one correspondence, since they might lay a meal table by matching a spoon, fork and knife, and so on, to each person's place. Notice, however, that this is not done by counting, and the idea of one-to-one correspondence must in fact precede the notion of number.

We shall consider in the following pages how we can nurture these seeds to help the child to understand the mathematical ideas we classify as arithmetic.

Properties of objects and the sets they form

Since the process of sorting and classifying is very natural for young children, it is important that activities which depend upon this are included in the early school experience. However, the purpose of introducing this in school is to provide a spring board for further development. It is therefore not sufficient to leave the child happily sorting plastic toys, bricks, etc., for hours and then to let him go out to play. The teacher must find time to talk to the child about what he has done and why he chose to do the job in a particular way. Early materials should be interesting collections of objects that can be sorted in a variety of different ways, either into piles or using sorting trays, thus encouraging the development of the child's perception and later his language as he talks about his work (or play). The teacher should remember that a well-chosen collection of ten or twelve objects is much more useful than an ill-chosen bag of fifty. In the discussion that the teacher will have with the child, some time should be devoted to discussion of why a particular object does *not* belong in some other collection than the one chosen by the child. The child might respond as follows: 'I have put all the red things together, all the yellow things together, all the green things together, so that green one belongs there.' He will probably need to be encouraged to see that the green boat does not belong with the red boats because by being green it is *not* red.

We must recognise, of course, that the needs of everyday language and the desires of adults for adequate vocabulary-building in their offspring tend to operate against the natural use of the negation of an attribute. For example, if the child sees a cow in a field, he will get little credit from an adult for saying that it is *not* a horse, and yet this recognition is almost as important. Take a coin from your pocket or purse and try to say as many things as you can about it. It is natural to select those attributes which can be used for positive identification: it is silver-coloured, is round, bears the Queen's head, is worth 10p, and so on; however, there is no reason why one should not now use negatives of attributes: it will *not* bend, it is *not* a 5p piece, it is *not* living, it is *not* edible, and so on. A moment's reflection will show that, at least intuitively, an object is *not* a great many more things than it is! In fact what you can say in negation of attributes is virtually limitless. At first sight this appears a futile activity; however, it is just as important to know what an object is *not* as it is to know what it is.

It will be realised that in order that children should be able to experience the full significance of the idea of attributes or properties and their negations, they need to be given plenty of experience with different collections of material. Each separate collection of material, whether it be a box of bricks, a bag of beads, an assortment of leaves, or nuts, or assorted random objects, the contents of a young boy's pocket, is described as a *universe*. Each universe can be as large or small as one pleases.

Suppose we have a random collection of material consisting of, say, the following nine objects:

a brass Yale-type key, a red wooden bead, a plastic soldier painted red, a black plastic pig, a clear green glass marble, a spent match, a brass curtain ring, a fir cone, a small flint pebble.

These will form our universe. An invitation to sort the objects may possibly produce a result something like this:

'Red' things
   wooden bead, plastic soldier
'Black' things
   plastic pig
'Brown' things
   fir cone

5

'Green' things
  marble
'Yellow' things
  key, curtain ring
'Grey' things
  flint pebble
'White' things
  match stick

You may not agree with the sorting described above, especially if you were to see the objects. If we examine closely the processes used, they owe their origins to the obsessive desire we have to find positive labels for things. Try to detach yourself from the sorting for a moment and analyse the steps needed to carry through the operation. First, we decide that there are red things, black things, and so on. Imagine now that we pick up the wooden bead. 'Ah, red,' we say; and then we turn to the toy soldier. In effect, we must ask the question, 'Is it red?' If the answer is 'Yes', it joins the bead, if 'No', we form a new set. For each successive object we have to answer the question, 'Does it belong to one of the sets we already have?' If it does not fit into any of the sets already in existence, we simply produce another one.

Sorting with reference to one attribute only

We could cut this complicated situation quite significantly by accepting that each object can be either 'red' or not. The 'red' objects form one *set*, the others 'not red' form the *complement* of the set. In this case we use just one question: each object is sorted into one of two sets by means of a single attribute, which the object either possesses or does not possess.

We can show this in other situations. Suppose we throw all the nine objects into a bowl of water and stir them around vigorously. We shall form two sets, one composed of those objects which float and the other of those which do *not* float. By using a simple test we can see which objects could be threaded on to string and those which *cannot*. In each case we have a set of objects each possessing the attribute and another complement set of objects not possessing the attribute.

In the first instance we should allow the children any method of sorting they choose, but we should aim to develop the idea of 'being red' or 'being not red' as a viable means of sorting. A bag with an assortment of many different coloured beads helps to bring this idea into the child's mind, since, if the red ones are taken out, the remainder will be 'other colours', that is, 'other colours than red', which means 'not red'.

An ideal material for sorting is the class of children themselves. Boys and girls (or boys and not boys), or children wearing glasses/not wearing glasses. These attributes are discriminating attributes, that is, they form well-defined sets. By this is meant that there is no doubt to which set each object belongs. If we use the attribute 'is wearing red/is not wearing red' to sort the children, we should have many more problems, for example, when does red cease to be red, and how much red is needed? A little thought makes it clear that an attribute which is discriminating in one universe might not be in another universe.

There are many ways of representing the sorting process. Perhaps the three most useful are the following:

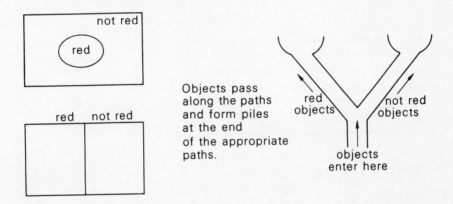

Sorting with reference to two attributes simultaneously

Suppose now we wish to sort the objects further with reference to a second attribute.

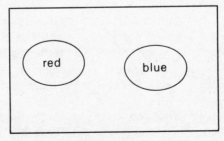

The objects outside the two loops will be those which belong neither

7

to the *red set* nor to the *blue set.*

This activity becomes much more interesting if we choose two attributes, both of which can be possessed by an object at the same time, say red/not red and float/not float. The sorting carried out in this manner can be represented in a variety of ways.

The *Venn diagram* representation is:

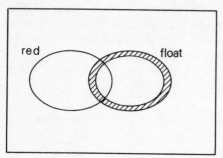

All '*red*' objects go inside the single loop.
All '*floaters*' go inside the double loop.
'*Red floaters*' go inside both loops.
'*Non-red, non-floaters*' go outside the loops but inside the 'box'.

The Carroll diagram

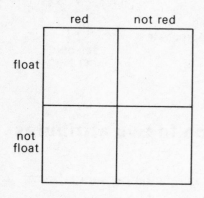

The labels apply to rows and columns respectively.

The Tree diagram

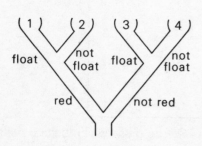

Objects pass along the paths of the tree according to their attributes. They finish as piles of objects placed at the end of each limb.
So (1) will be the set of 'red floaters' and (4) will be the set of 'not red not floaters', etc.

If the choice of attribute leads to a situation in which no object possesses the attribute, we have what is called an *empty set*, which has no members; for example, if we take as our universe a class of children, the set of those children with four legs would be an *empty set*.

Note: The ideas contained in this section are fundamental; however discretion should be used when deciding the point at which expressions like *universe*, *empty set*, *complement* may be introduced.

2 Logic Blocks and Other Structured Systems

The introduction of a structured system

The material suggested for the activities described in the previous chapter may be carefully chosen, but it would still be described as unstructured. Let us consider the following universal set of material, comprising twelve plastic shapes which could also be used for sorting in similar ways.

Key   r=red   y=yellow   w=white   g=green

Each object has many different attributes. We notice that some of these attributes are especially important; for instance, it can be seen that the colour of an object is important, since any two boats are identical apart from colour. The other important attribute might be called the shape (i.e. boat, teddy-bear, or doll), since two objects can be the same colour but different shapes. When children are at home with the activities described earlier, it is important that they meet material like this, in

which certain attributes determine the collection of material. To understand this better, suppose the doll marked 'X' is missing. Most children
would be able to notice this very quickly, even if it had never been present.
Not only could they say that one of the objects is missing, but also they
could give an accurate description of its attributes. The collection of
material described in the previous chapter could easily have an object
missing with little or no hope of it being noticed, since we can only
identify membership of the set by pure memory. It would be quite impossible to identify a missing piece that we had never seen at all.

Clearly the universal set of objects (dolls, boats and teddy-bears) has
a system (or structure) to it. We should be able to describe this structure
in some way. However, before we proceed further, it should be noted
that the following discussion would not be suitable for many (if any)
children in the infant school. There are clearly two *variables*, colour and
'shape'. One of these variables can take any of four different *values* (red
yellow, white and green). The other variable can take any of three different
values (boat, bear, doll). Thus we can describe the system as being a
4×3 system (4 values for one independent variable and 3 values for a
second independent variable). In this structured system we have traded
the large variety of random attributes of the first type of material for a
very few carefully chosen attributes.

The Dienes Logic Blocks*

Further progress is difficult unless we have a structured system with
more variables. However, increasing the number of variables and having
all possible combinations of these produces an undesirable increase in
the number of objects (elements) in the universal set. A reasonable
compromise between these conflicting aims can be found in the Dienes
Logic Blocks.

It will be seen that there are 48 pieces made up from 4 shape values,
3 colour values, 2 thickness values and 2 size values. The reader should
have little difficulty in identifying this as a $4 \times 3 \times 2 \times 2$ system with 4
different variables.

---

* Dienes Logic Blocks (sold under the name Logiblocs) can be obtained from ESA
Creative Learning Limited, Pinnacles, P.O. Box 22, Harlow, Essex.

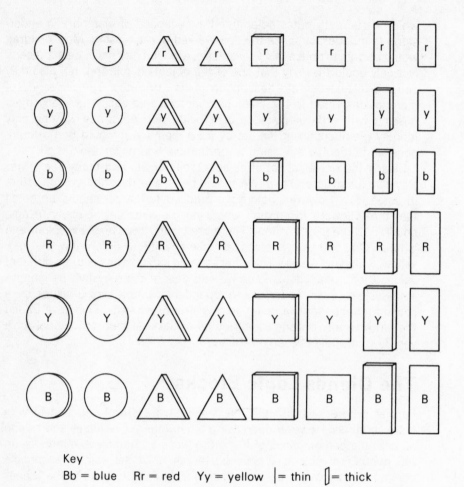

Key

Bb = blue   Rr = red   Yy = yellow | = thin   ◫ = thick

Subsystems of Logic Blocks

It is important for the teacher to be able to form smaller systems from the 48 blocks of the complete universe of Logic Blocks. During the early stages of using the blocks children sometimes find the complete universe too complex, but by reducing the number of dimensions and/or the values of each variable, the number of blocks is also reduced while preserving the essential idea of a system.

LOGIC BLOCKS AND OTHER STRUCTURED SYSTEMS

e.g. 12 blocks as a 4×3 system.

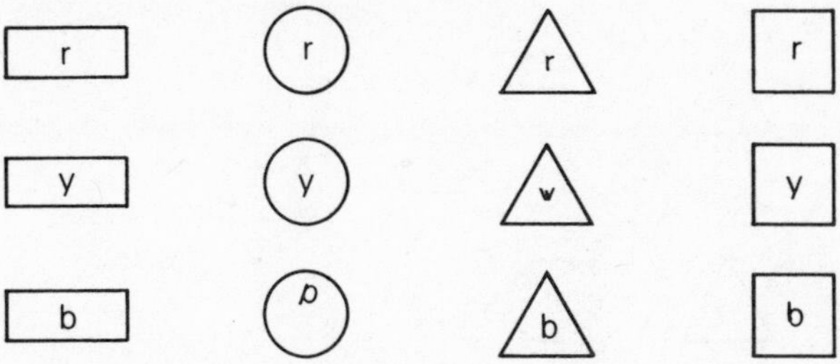

4 shapes
3 colours
all one thickness
and one size

or 12 blocks as a 3×2×2 system.

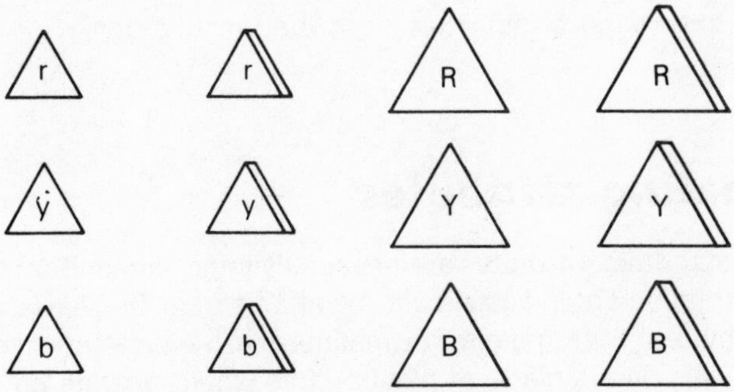

3 colours
2 sizes
2 thicknesses
all one shape

There are alternative 3×2×2 systems.

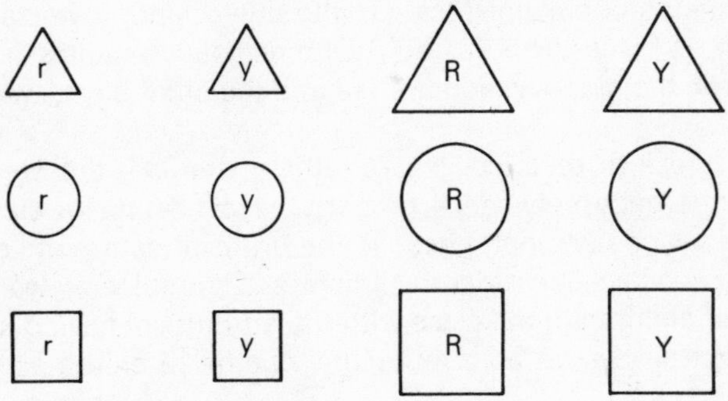

3 shapes
2 colours
2 sizes
all one thickness

8 blocks as 4×2 system.

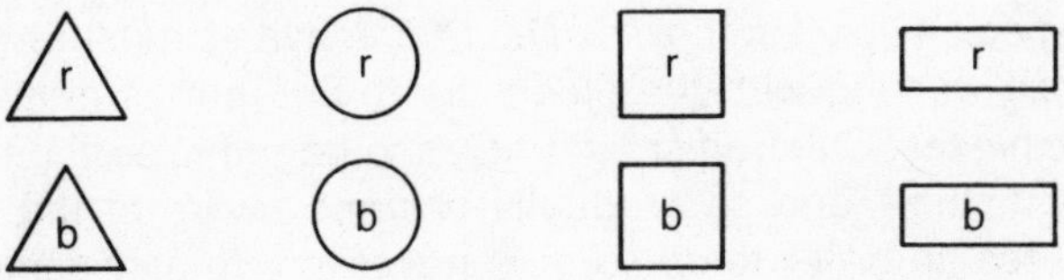

4 shapes
2 colours
all one thickness
and one size

8 blocks as 2×2×2 system.

2 shapes
2 colours
2 thicknesses
all one size

etc.

Forming these subsets is a useful activity for older children when they have completed the range of activities described in this book.

Discriminating attributes

Again we see that certain attributes are especially important and provide us with real information about a particular block. We must be clear about what we mean by real information. For instance, if we pick up a Logic Block and say, 'This one is made of plastic', this would provide no real information which enables us to distinguish this block from any other block in our universe. In other words, being plastic is a universal characteristic of the elements of our universe. On the other hand, if we select an attribute such as 'This block is red', it immediately enables us to distinguish between the blocks which are red and the other blocks which are not.

One advantage of using Logic Blocks after other material is that we are able to see the difference between a property which defines a subset precisely and one which does not, because the artificial nature of Logic Blocks is specially conceived in order to eliminate this problem. If we use the universal set of children in the class with the attribute of having light hair, we should not always be able to decide whether a child has this attribute or not.

In meeting the Logic Blocks for the first time, it is essential that learners of any age are given the blocks in a random form. They should not be presented in the specially packed boxes. The first activities must be free play, in which those working with the blocks try to find out as much as they can about the pieces. Children should be encouraged to sort out the blocks, to talk about them and so gradually become aware of the discriminating attributes. In order to do so, it is necessary to play some of

14

the basic familiarisation games such as those suggested below.

a) Picture making

Frequently, children like to make 'pictures' with the blocks, for example:

If the 'picture' is almost entirely composed of blocks of, say, one colour, or one size or one thickness, it is usually possible to encourage the child to make the 'picture' entirely of blocks of one colour/size/thickness. (It is, of course, difficult to get more than one of these fixed at a time except in the most simple 'pictures'.)

Suppose the figure above is made from all thin blocks, the child might now be asked to construct a 'fat' figure like the original, this time using only thick blocks.

Many variations are possible, for example:

b) Engine

Arrange yellow pieces as follows:

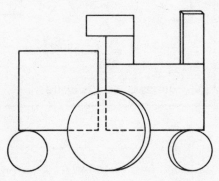

The children can be invited to make the same engine in red, and also to make the same engine in blue, but going in the other direction, which is considerably more difficult.

Other pictures can be made with *rules of change* to go with them. It is frequently possible to use something a child has already made as a model to be repeated in this way (houses, petrol stations, trees, boats, etc.), and this is almost always better than setting a particular problem.

c) Hiding a block

The teacher or one of the children hides a block while all the others close their eyes. The first child who can correctly identify the block by all its attributes wins it back.

Another version of this game requires one child to look at a block and think about its attributes. The other children then ask questions about its attributes in the form of 'Is it red?', to which the answer will be either 'Yes' or 'No'. The object of the game is to decide on all four attributes of the block as quickly as possible. Some children are able to develop quite good strategies for this at an early stage. For example, if the answer to the question 'Is it red?' is 'No', only one further question about colour is required in order to establish this attribute without doubt. Many children find it helpful to have a chart on which the following information is inscribed:

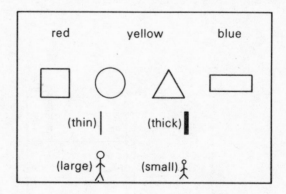

If the answer to the question 'Is it red?' is 'No', the red label is covered with a small piece of card

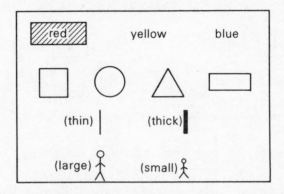

If the answer is 'Yes', cards are used to cover the words yellow and blue.

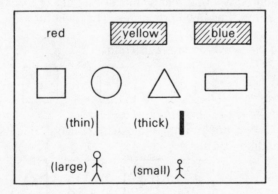

The properties of the block are uniquely determined when four labels remain uncovered. (This requires a maximum of seven questions, but a more lenient approach might allow young children a maximum of ten questions, since they may well waste questions by saying 'Is it red?'— 'No'; 'Is it blue?'—'No'; 'Is it yellow?'—'Yes'.)

d) Games with Logicubes*

Logicubes are a set of four dice. The first is inscribed on three pairs of faces with the colours of the blocks, the second is likewise inscribed with the shapes (two being repeated), the third has three faces marked

'thin' ⬚ and three marked 'thick' , ⬚ and the fourth has its

faces marked 'large' ⬚ and 'small' ⬚

If one die only is thrown, say that with different colour faces, and the

face marked ⬚ r appears uppermost, the children can then collect

together all the blocks with this property. This collection will be the *set* of *red* blocks.

If a second die is added, the display might now be:

The children will find that a smaller number of blocks than before can be found with these two properties. They will form the set of *large blue* blocks.

A third die is even more restricting;

will yield the set of *small thin yellow* blocks.

If all four dice are brought into use there is only one block to satisfy this set of conditions. Thus:

fixes the four attributes, limiting the collection to a single block—the *large thick red triangle*.

The dice help the children to realise the unique nature of each object in the universe.

* Logicubes can be obtained from ESA Creative Learning Limited.

e) Wall game

This is a game for two children, or two pairs of children, who sit on opposite sides of a table, down the centre of which is a solid screen. Two halves of a set of logic blocks, chosen in a random way, are placed on each side of the screen. As a consequence the child (or children) on one side can only see some of the blocks. The object of the game is to win pieces from the other side of the screen. This is achieved by the children asking in turn for any block which is in the possession of their opponent(s); they must, however, ask for the block by an accurate description of all its attributes, for example, 'Pass me the large thin blue triangle.' If this piece is available, it must be passed over the screen.

The game is useful for young children in helping them to describe correctly the properties of an object which they cannot see. Often they will either fail to describe correctly the block they require, or will describe a block which is already in their possession! It is sometimes necessary to. add a rule which prohibits the same block from passing backwards and forwards over the screen.

f) Houses

Firstly, the children are given the six large triangles, which they are asked to arrange touching one another as closely as possible and so that there are no two of the same colour or thickness together (the best arrangement is a hexagon).

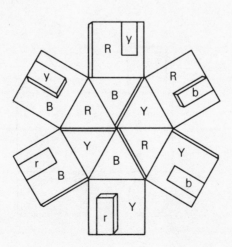

When this is completed successfully, they are given the six large squares which they are asked to place below the triangles (to form houses) so they are as different as possible from the triangles. Then the six small rectangles are to be placed on the squares to form front doors to the houses, so they are as different as possible.

The children can then be invited to arrange the houses so that there are three on one side of the road and three on the other. It is suggested that the houses next to each other should be of different colours (walls, roofs, doors). However, dismantling houses is not allowed.

This game can be developed in many ways. For example, trees can be formed by using large circles as foliage, large rectangles for the trunks and small circles as birds' nests in the trees. It should then be possible to associate a tree with each house. The pairing of the first tree with a house will fix the rest of the pairings, if the matching is to be consistent throughout. The children might then add 'dog kennels' from the remaining squares and triangles using any rule of their own choice.

g) Meal tables

From the Logic Blocks use: 3 large thick rectangles
3 each small thick rectangles
squares
triangles
circles

Take first the yellow pieces and, using the large rectangle as the table, put the other pieces, two each side, to be people sitting at the breakfast table.

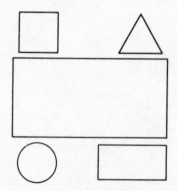

Now take the red pieces to form the lunch table. However, when the people sit down to lunch they must not sit next to the person they were next to at breakfast, nor opposite the person they were opposite at breakfast.

Finally, the blue pieces form the tea table. Again the people take their places, but not next to anyone they have sat next to before, nor opposite anyone to whom they have been opposite before.

Simple relational games

Children should play plenty of games in which they describe the attributes of blocks and sort them into sets with chosen attributes. Slowly they should be led on to noticing that some blocks possess a particular attribute which others do not. For example, one member of the group picks out two blocks and asks in how many ways are these blocks alike and in how many ways are they different, and to say as much as possible about them. This should be done a number of times until the children are really familiar with them and able to state each time the four attributes involved. Another activity which is useful at this stage is for one person to pick out a block and a partner to select, on instruction from the first person, a block which is different from the first in 1, 2, 3 or 4 ways, or, alternatively, to find a block which is like the first one in 1, 2, 3 or 4 ways.

As soon as the children are familiar with the attributes that we are using, we can talk a little more about the idea of an attribute such as redness, which enables us to distinguish a set within the universe. We can then talk about the blocks which are left and come round to the idea of the complement of our set, that is to say, that if we establish a defining attribute which creates a set within the blocks, we immediately also define a complementary set of blocks which do not have this attribute, a set of red blocks—a set of *not* red blocks. It is important to notice that *yellow* is not equivalent to *not red* while *thin* is equivalent to *not thick*. In this discussion we should, of course, also mention the idea of the empty set as the complement of the universe.

One of the games which can usefully be played at this stage with the children is the so-called 'Cross-Roads' game. For those who are not familiar with the game, it is best seen with the help of the illustration below. The roads can be given any names which one chooses, for instance, if the north-south road is called the Square Road and the east-west road is the Red Road then the blocks can be placed in the road where they 'live' so that those in the centre satisfy the necessary conditions. This would be described as a *conjunction* situation because the main emphasis lies in finding the correct pieces which will have the properties of being both red and square. The roads on the sheets given to pupils should not be labelled with particular titles, but the children should be left completely free to select these in order that they can explore the problems arising from calling one road 'Red' and the other one 'Blue', for instance.

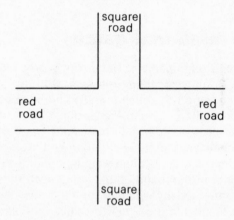

Venn, Carroll and Tree diagrams

The diagrams suggested earlier for use with the unstructured sets of material can be usefully re-introduced at this stage. Three diagrams of different types to accommodate sets of blocks with the properties of being blue or not blue, circular or not circular, are given below.

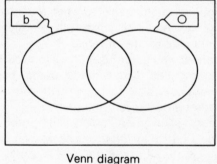

Venn diagram

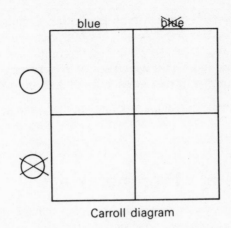

Carroll diagram

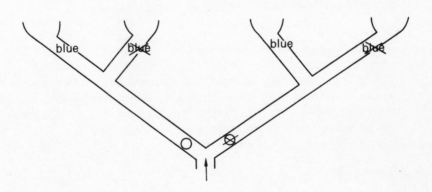

It is important for the children to recognise that each of these is simply a different representation of the same idea. This will not be achieved by telling them so, but by helping them to see that each has four equivalent regions. This can be done by asking the children to move all the blocks from one diagram to another; initially it is very likely that the blocks will be transferred singly but after a short time they will notice that all the blocks in one region of one diagram occupy the corresponding region in the second diagram, and they will thus be able to move the blocks by sets and not as singles.

Notice that even the Venn diagram has four regions, the fourth being that part which lies outside the two loops but inside the outer boundary.

The children should also be asked questions such as:

(i) 'Where are the blocks which are both blue and circular?'
(ii) 'Where are the blocks which are both not blue and circular?'
(iii) 'Where are the blocks which are both blue and not circular?'
(iv) 'Where are the blocks which are both not blue and not circular?'
(v) 'Where are the blocks which are not both blue and circular?'

No two of these questions are equivalent. The last includes all the three preceding it, (ii), (iii), (iv), since it is everything which is not included in (i), that is, 44 blocks in all.

The use of other materials

While a great deal of emphasis has been placed upon the use of Logic Blocks for the work described above, it is very necessary for the child to meet other materials which are structured systems with different attributes. Some examples of these are given below.

People Logic Set*

This set consists of plastic models of human figures in four colours (red, yellow, blue, green), in three positions (sitting, walking and standing), male and female, adult and child. It is again a 4×3×2×2 system and can be used in just the same ways as the Logic Blocks.

Trimath†

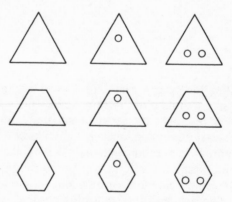

---

* The People Logic Set can be obtained from ESA Creative Learning Limited.

† Both the Trimath and the Quadrimath sets can be obtained from ESA Creative Learning Limited.

This set comprises 54 pieces made to a 6×3×3 system. There are six colours (red, yellow, blue, green, white, black). The shapes appear in each of the six colours.

Quadrimath

The 64 pieces of the 4×4×4 Quadrimath set are in four colours (red, yellow, blue, green), with four shapes and four different hole arrangements as illustrated below.

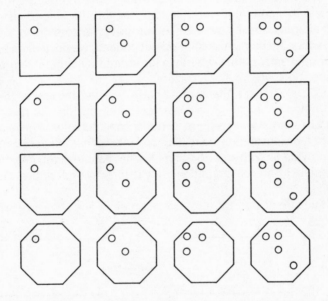

Both the Trimath and Quadrimath sets can be used in a similar way to the Logic Blocks, although the systems are not made up in the same way as they each have only three independent variables instead of the four found in the Logic Blocks and People Logic Set.

3 States and Operators

Introducing 'machines'

In Chapter 5 (page 41) we shall be looking at the kinds of relations which can exist between two objects. For example,

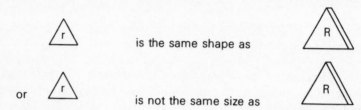

is the same shape as

or

is not the same size as

However, there is a group of activities which provide a useful preliminary to this and later work. Let us consider the idea of taking an object and altering one or more of its attributes according to some specific instruction to define a second object. Indeed, we have already considered this in the early games when we looked at the 'engine' to be remade in a different colour.

To develop these ideas more fully, we can introduce the 'machine'. Our 'machine' is simply an abstract idea, but like its real life counterparts it operates according to quite specific rules. For example, if we insert the appropriate coin (say 5p) into a milk dispensing machine, it will provide us with a carton of milk. The machine can only do what it was designed to do, on condition that it is provided with a suitable input (say 5p).

A suitable design for our abstract machine is shown below.

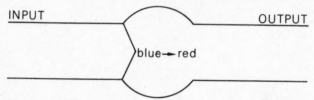

The instruction (or *operator*) in the centre means, alter the *blue* property of the input block (or *input state*) into the *red* property for the output block (or *output state*). The blocks, however, must be the same in every other way. If we place a *blue* large thin triangle in the input, the output must be a *red* large thin triangle; we show this as:

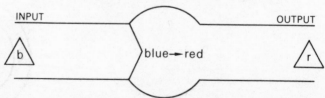

The original *blue* piece is not lost, but its insertion releases a corresponding *red* piece.

This is like a 5p milk machine. We all know that inserting a 5p piece releases 1 carton of milk; the 5p piece is *not* magically transformed into milk. Most people are completely disinterested in the internal workings of a milk machine so long as it delivers the milk! The same applies to our machines. However, like the milk machine, the input has to be acceptable, it would be useless trying to insert a 1p piece or a 10p in a slot designed for 5p pieces, similarly a 'blue → red' machine rejects all yellow objects and also all *red* ones. (Have you ever tried pouring milk in through the coin slot of a milk machine?)

The children should be given a wide range of experiences with similar machines, using a variety of material. It is, however, important that they realise the difference between machine operators which produce a single output object and those for which a set of solutions is possible.

An operator of the kind 'blue → red' is called a *function*. This is because there is a uniquely determined output for any input. Using a set of logic blocks to provide the inputs and outputs, we could make a *relation* machine by choosing a less specific operator such as 'change colour'. In this case we should have a *solution set* for any given input block, thus a *blue* large thin triangle input would yield either a *yellow* or *red* large thin triangle as an output, since no other attribute is altered. The reader will no doubt realise that for the purposes of this work we may regard *functions* as a subset of *relations*.

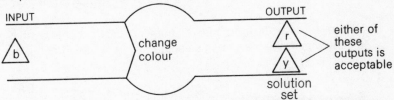

When several blocks have been fed into the machine, it is possible to compare which blocks on the output side correspond to particular blocks on the input side.

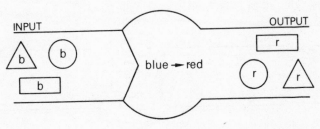

A one-to-one correspondence can then be established between the input and output sides.

Input/output tables

An extension of this activity is the use of a table to display the one-to-one correspondence.

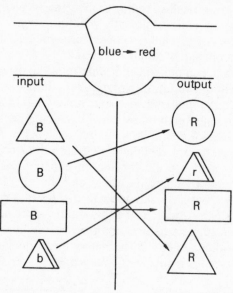

Here we are showing the relationship between pairs of blocks, the second one in the pair being selected by noting the effect of the operator on the first.

More versatile operators

When the idea of selecting the right kind of input for the machine is understood, it is possible to make the operator more universal in its application, that is, to accept any logic block. This is done as follows:

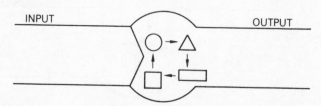

This operator means that a circle input gives a triangle output

a triangle input gives a rectangle output

a rectangle input gives a square output

a square input gives a circle output

Of course, all other attributes remain unchanged.

Hence a small thin red *triangle input* gives

a small thin red *rectangle output*.

A possible arrangement of input/output blocks is illustrated below:

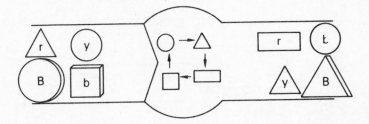

The reader should have little difficulty in establishing the one-to-one correspondence between the input block and the appropriate output block.

This is more clearly seen if we use the table as before:

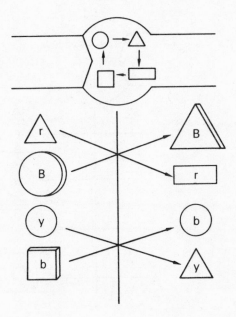

Several interesting variations on this idea are possible. The table below requires the child to find a suitable output block in each case:

Table i

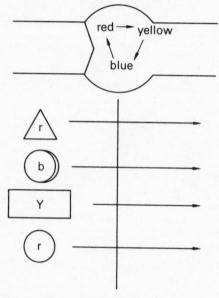

The next requires him to find the input which would yield the given output:

Table ii

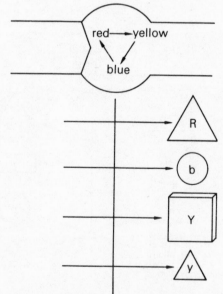

and finally, the most challenging, to find the operator which links the inputs and outputs in the following manner:

Table iii

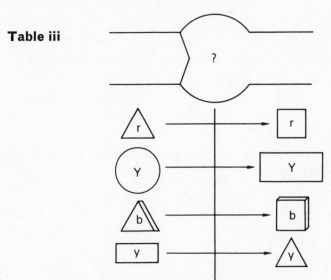

Applications to arithmetic — a projection ahead

To reassure the reader who feels that we have lost all contact with the familiar ground of traditional mathematics, it is perhaps useful to show how closely the function machine relates to arithmetic.

Let us suppose we have a machine which dispenses 3 sweets on the insertion of a 1p coin. This can be displayed in the same way as the machines above.

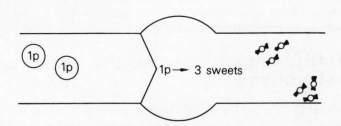

The tables shown above correspond to questions of the following kinds:

Table i — For any given input what is the output?
or 'If I put in 4p how many sweets will I get?'

Table ii — For any given output what is the corresponding input?
or 'How much do I need to put in to get 9 sweets?'

Table iii — What is the operator?
or 'The label has fallen off the machine, by putting money in and counting the sweets I get out, can I find out what the machine does?'

In more sophisticated terms the three tables can be likened to three arithmetic problems:

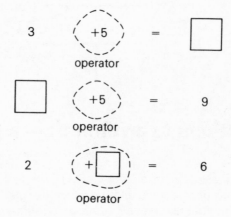

The teacher should not be tempted to introduce these sophisticated machines at too early a stage. The purpose of the development described in this book is to give a sound foundation of ideas, using material with which the child is familiar in situations which he can control. We shall see later how the arithmetic ideas can grow from these experiences.

Multiple machines and the use of coded instructions

In order to develop the child's understanding of the machine idea, it is desirable to introduce some more demanding problems. Children enjoy the added complication formed by joining two machines together in series, viz.

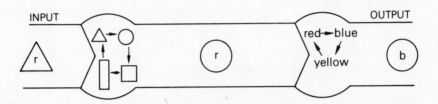

Here the output of the first machine becomes the input of the second. Thus an input of a red triangle becomes an intermediate output (from the first machine) of a red circle, which on entering the second machine, releases a blue circle. The complexity can be increased further as follows:

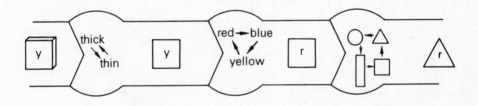

The activity involves deciding (a) which attribute has to be changed; (b) how that particular attribute changes.

Another state and operator game of this kind, which is very popular, makes use of movable arrows. Say we make use of two colours of arrows (black and white) which have the following meanings:

The first player places a block on the floor and follows it by one of the arrows, e.g.

The second player now finds the correct block to follow the operator arrow and then chooses another operator arrow for the third player:

The third and subsequent players continue in like manner. The game ends when no further piece can be played (because it has been used before) whichever colour arrow is used. The play might be as follows:

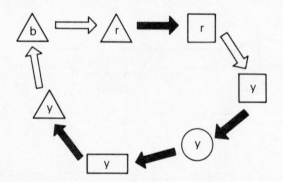

The game needs a lot of thought for young children, but when they have mastered it they often enjoy (and suggest) using another colour arrow to mean change size (or thickness). An alternative development makes use of several arrows between the blocks.

There are many possible ways of developing this further, for example, look for redundant sequences of arrows (⟹ ⟹ ⟹ is 'do nothing'), or place two blocks and decide which arrows will be needed for the smallest length operator to go between the first and the second block.

4 Properties of Sets; Sets of Sets

Number as a property of a set

The next step is to establish the ideas we have seen so far with sets of objects. Clearly we can look at a set of things and notice attributes particular to the set, rather than attributes of the discrete objects. For example, in a set of top juniors, properties of the set might be *eight children*, *three boys* and *five girls*, *all over 1·45 metres tall*, *all under 12 years of age*, and so on.

Perhaps the most important of these properties of sets is the idea of number. Five cannot be shown except by displaying sets of five objects; we arrive at the idea of five only through seeing lots of members of the set of *sets of five objects*. For ease of conversation we say that the following sets:

 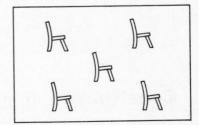

 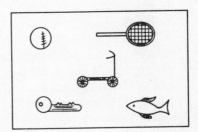

belong to the 'five club'. Clearly these sets have to have a very special attribute to belong to the five club. So we are at the point of realising that not only do single objects have attributes, but sets of objects also have attributes which enable them to belong to clubs.

We must emphasise that this idea of a set belonging to the five club is neither better nor worse than a set belonging to the three club. At the early stage we are only providing experience to help in understanding that the three club is different from the five club. *Later* we come to the idea of more than and less than, which we can achieve quite easily by one-to-one matching—the idea of a relation. *Even later* we come to the idea of two more and two less, and so on.

Clearly we cannot use this sort of sophisticated discussion with children (particularly infants), but we can provide experience of these 'clubs' or 'families' from which they can form their own ideas.

By preparing systems of sets (as described below), just as we have systems of objects, and by giving the children opportunities to play some of the simple games mentioned earlier, we hope to focus attention on the attributes of sets.

We can also try relating sets to sets in a simple way, e.g. using a set of books, a set of children, a set of chairs. Are there enough books for the children, or too many perhaps? Are there enough chairs for the children to sit on, or the right number? This need not necessarily be done by counting, as it can best be resolved by the idea of one-to-one correspondence, or attempted matching (for example, get the children to sit on the chairs: are there enough? Are there some left over? Are there just the right number?).

Construction of systems of sets

It is vital that children see that relationships can exist between sets in the same way that they can between objects like Logic Blocks. We need to be able to construct sets for the children to use which have attributes in the same way that objects have attributes.

As explained earlier, the standard set of Logic Blocks has 4 shapes, 3 colours, 2 sizes and 2 thicknesses. Such a system is described as being 4×3×2×2. Suppose we select all large, thick blocks; this will give 12 pieces (4 shapes and 3 colours), which would then be a 4×3 system. Of course, 12 pieces need not be a 4×3 system; they could form a 3×2×2 system which would happen if we took just the square blocks (say). Within the set of Logic Blocks it is clearly possible to extract systems meeting many needs (e.g. 2×2×2×2—use only two shapes, two colours, two thicknesses, two sizes; or 3×3×2, or 4×3×2, or 4×2×2 etc. etc.— see page 12).

Let us return to the 4×3 system. Suppose now we wish to establish a system of sets to illustrate the same idea. Clearly one attribute of the sets must vary in four ways (compare 4 shapes in Logic Blocks). Let us suppose that we decide to show this by having either zero, one, two, or three soldiers stuck to otherwise identical pieces of card. The other attribute must vary in 3 ways (compare 3 colours in Logic Blocks) and we decide to show this by having either no animal on the card, or one dog, or one horse. So each card can have as one of its attributes either 0, 1, 2, or 3 soldiers, and the other attribute, a dog, a horse, or nothing.

How then should we prepare the cards? It is perhaps easiest if we lay out the cards in a 4×3 framework as below.

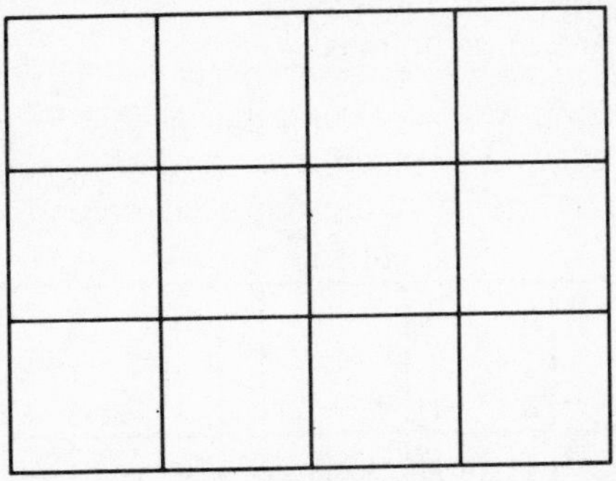

Now each column must be different from the other column so we arrange to have soldiers placed as shown.

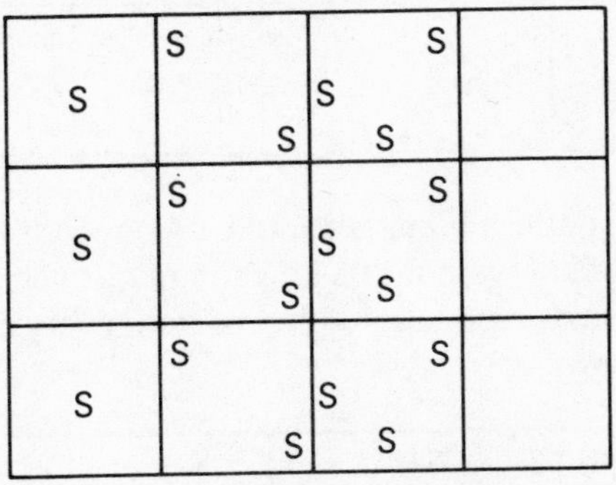

	S		S
S		S	
	S	S	
	S		S
S		S	
	S	S	
	S		S
S		S	
	S	S	

S means one soldier

Now to fix the other attribute. We make each row different from each other row as shown.

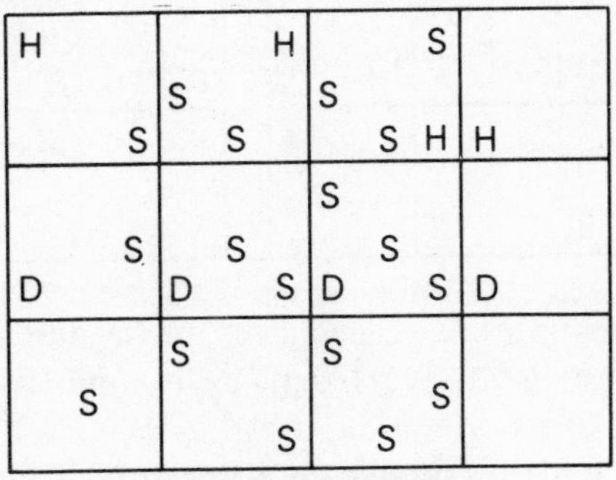

H		H	S
	S	S	
S	S	S H	H
		S	
S	S	S	
D	D	S D	S D
	S	S	
S			S
	S	S	

S means one soldier
H means one horse
D means one dog

The system is now complete, since no card is the same as any other card. Remember the blank card belongs because it has:

(a) the attribute of no soldiers;
(b) the attribute of no animal.

Suppose now we wish to extend this system to a 4×3×2. This time we lay out 24 cards, and proceed to arrange the sets as before; however, we repeat this for the second group of 12 cards as shown.

Now we must add the last attribute which we might show by adding a red button or not. If we put this on each of our second group of 12 cards, we shall now have every card different from every other card in a 4×3×2 system, as shown.

The same procedure is followed for any systems, although attributes can be shown in many ways (e.g. by number of items, by shape, by colour, and so on).

It is probably better to fix objects to the cards, which then form a system of sets of objects, rather than to make drawings. We hope the children will disregard the card and concentrate on the objects. In the case of drawings, it is more natural to think about the card as the main ingredient of the system.

The activities which have been described in the previous sections, using logic blocks and other attribute material, should also be repeated with this and other systems of sets. For example, a suitable machine might be constructed with the operator

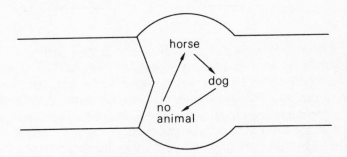

which could be used with the cards as shown. In this case, only the 'animal' property is changed between the input and output cards. Thus an input card with a horse will yield a corresponding output card with a dog. The number of soldiers, or the presence or absence of a button, will not be affected by this operator.

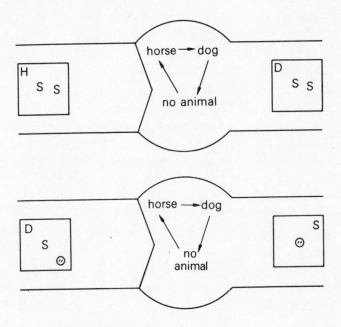

It is also important to notice the nature of likeness and difference with this material. If we examine the two cards:

we observe that these cards are alike in that they both have a dog on them, they are also alike in that neither of them has a button. However, they are different in just one way because the first has soldiers and the second has not. The possession of a number of soldiers is not better than possessing few or none, it is merely different. Each card (in relation to the whole set) has just three attributes. In the pair chosen above, two of these attributes are alike, the remaining one is different.

5 Relations of Likeness, Difference and Order

Attribute statements and relation statements

When children have come to realise the importance of attributes we can turn to the next stage of our discussion which can be the development of the idea of relation.

A single object can have an attribute, so we say

... is a triangle.

So can a set of objects

... has five cows in it.

However, when we introduce a relation, we need to *relate* one object with another (or one set with another).

... is the same shape as ...

... has the same number of cows as ...

So we see that an attribute statement has only one place keeper while a relation has two.

Clearly there are different kinds of relations (equality, greater than, and so on), but it is easier to begin with simple relations between the familiar objects and sets the children have been meeting.

Take Logic Blocks, for example. There are relations of the kind '... is the same colour as ...', which is a '*likeness*' relation. Then, of course, comes the '*difference*' relation:—'... is *not* the same thickness as ...' Then we encounter '*order*' relations:—'... is thicker than ...' or '... has more sides than ...' The same ideas can be seen in relations between sets. We can begin by establishing relations of order and so on between pairs of objects or sets.

Many people have considerable difficulty in identifying 'order' relations and 'difference' relations. Certain points must always be remembered.

(1) A 'difference' relation merely says that two objects or sets are not the same; an 'order' relation makes a judgment about a quality of that difference (better than, if you like).

(2) A 'difference' relation is reversible; that is, if △ is not the same shape as ☐, then ☐ is not the same shape as △. An 'order' relation is never reversible unless the relation itself is changed.

(3) Most 'orders' established by successive application of an 'order' relation on pairs of objects or sets are generally arbitrary; the alphabet is a good example, for the order is conventional, not absolute.

As before, we cannot expect the children to see the importance of these ideas by telling them. Hence we have more 'games'.

Difference games

(a) Using a 3×2 system (e.g. logic blocks of 3 shapes and 2 colours), place the pieces one to a space so that the conditions are satisfied. There are a number of different but correct ways of arranging the blocks to satisfy the given conditions.

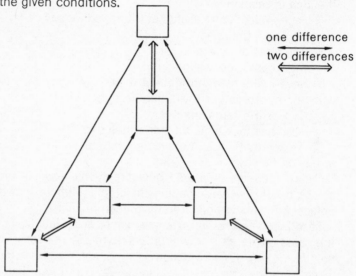

one difference
two differences

(b) Using a 4×2 system (e.g. logic blocks of 4 shapes and 2 thicknesses), place the pieces one to a space so that the conditions are satisfied.

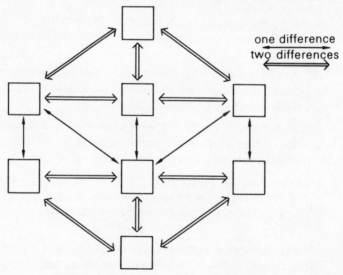

one difference
two differences

This diagram can also be filled with the system of sets cards described in Chapter 4, pages 36–8, using the 8 cards which do not have an animal (for example).

(c) Using a 2×2×2 system (e.g. logic blocks of 2 shapes, 2 colours and 2 sizes), place the pieces one to a space so that the conditions are satisfied.

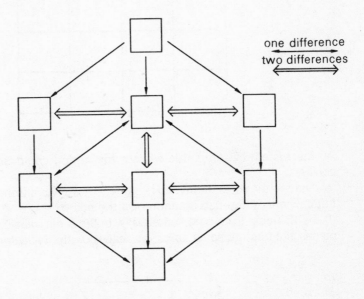

Again this diagram can be filled with the system of sets cards. A suitable collection would be the following:

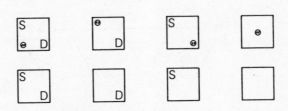

It will be found that the systems in games (b) and (c) are not interchangeable.

(d) Using 12 blocks (4 shapes and 3 colours), place these on a lattice of 12 compartments so that no two blocks of the same shape or same colour are next to each other (horizontally or vertically) anywhere on the board.

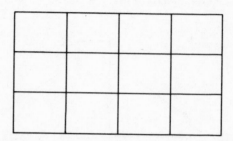

All the system of sets cards without the button could be used for this activity.

(e) Change the rules in the above game to have two differences sideways but only one difference up and down the board.

(f) Try 12 blocks (3 colours, 4 shapes) with the same rules (*no* two adjacent pieces shall be the same colour or shape) on the following diagram:

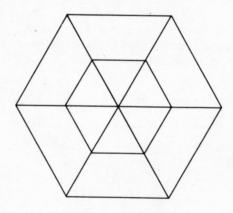

Also try a 3×4 set of sets on the same diagram.

(g) Using a 4×3×2 system, place the objects or sets on an enlarged version of the following diagram, one to a space. Each arrow shows a difference of *one* kind only.

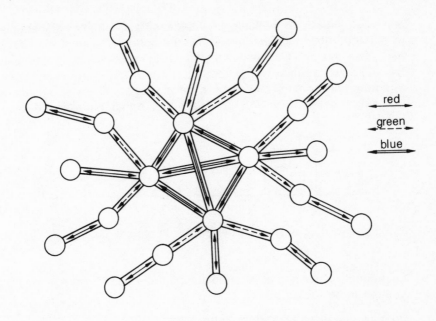

Should you decide (using logic blocks) that a blue arrow means a difference of shape, all blue arrows will link pieces which differ in shape only. Red arrows cannot show a difference of shape as this must mean something else. Another version of this game uses the blue arrows to indicate a difference of one attribute only, green arrows to indicate a difference in two attributes only and red arrows to indicate a difference in all three attributes.

h) Dominoes

A useful group of activities based on difference relations include the well-known domino games. These are particularly useful for older children, when they can be used as introductory games; however, young children also derive a great deal of pleasure from these activities. The simplest of these is the one difference domino game, ideal when played by 3, 4, or 5 people.

The first player puts down any piece out of the set, the next puts down a piece which is different from the first piece in one attribute only. The second piece can be played on either side of the first piece and the next player puts down a third piece. This piece can be played on either side

45

of the pair already on the table, provided it differs from the adjacent piece by one attribute only. Each player has the right to challenge the correctness of any piece. This means that if a player believes that another player has put down a piece which does not differ in the required number of attributes only from the piece before, he can say so. If he wins a challenge, he gains a point; if he wrongly challenges another player, he loses a point.

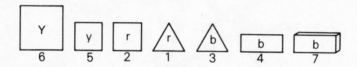

(numbers indicate possible order of play in typical game)

Each time a piece is placed unchallenged, the player scores a point. So points can be scored by:

(a) playing a piece according to the rules;
(b) discovering that the opponent has broken the rules.

The advantage of this method of play is that it encourages everyone to concentrate on the game even when it is not their turn to play. This game can also be played with 2, 3, or 4 differences.

A harder version of this game is one in which the pieces can be played in one direction only and in which the differences vary. Ideally one requires either 3 or 5 players for this game, but certainly not 4. The first player puts down any piece of his choice against either the edge of the table or a certain 'stop line'. The second player places a piece adjoining this which differs in one attribute only from the piece which has been played first. The third player now has to put a piece down which differs in two attributes from the one which has just been played, and so on until as many pieces as possible have been used. This is a more difficult situation because each time a player has a turn the number of different attributes—the differences that he is looking for—changes. It is also much more difficult to concentrate on the game and to detect errors of play. The same points system can be operated as suggested in the previous game.

Summary

We have discussed some of the ideas of likeness and difference. Of course, these ideas generally appear together and difference games must include some realisation of likeness. We have, so far, only touched on the order relation. These very important ideas will get fuller coverage in a later section.

Remember that all the activities described so far can be played with other systems of attribute material—the People Logic Set pieces, Trimath and Quadrimath,* and so on, and, of course, the sets of sets described in Chapter 4, pages 36–8.

* These systems can be obtained from ESA Creative Learning Limited.

6 Equivalence Relations and Equivalence Classes

A very important relation in mathematics grows out of the likeness relation. If we consider the relation '... has the same colour as ...' applied to logic blocks, we discover that in starting with one block and going through all the others in turn, they either satisfy the relation or not. Suppose we start with a large, thick red square, each successive piece will either be red, in which case we could put it in a pile with our first piece; or it will be blue (say), when we shall need to start a new pile; or yellow, when again a new pile is needed.

This relation is satisfied within quite large sets taken from the universe. If we consider all the red blocks, each pair will satisfy one relation, and similarly with the yellows or blues. However, the blocks which satisfy this relation are in clearly defined sets; it is not possible for a block to satisfy this relation and be in two sets (red and blue, say) at the same time. A relation which divides the members of a set in this way is called an equivalence relation and the sets formed by the equivalence relation are called equivalence classes.

Like our other relations, the equivalence relation depends on second order abstraction. If we put down six red blocks and ask the children to put down the blocks that belong with these, we should not be surprised if they stop after putting together the sixteen red blocks. If we are more careful to say that we want blocks put together so that they are alike in the same kind of way as these are alike, we may have a little more success. In fact, it is probably easier to play a sort of guessing game, in which you start with a few blocks and put them down to form equivalence classes (e.g. '... has the same shape *and* thickness as ...') in compartments on a large sheet, inviting the children to add other blocks as soon as they can see how it is being done. You remove any blocks which do not satisfy your relation.

A relation which is an equivalence relation when considering one set may well be only a likeness relation with another set. Consider the relation '... has the same colour as ...' with a set of a dozen necklaces each made from two colours of beads out of a choice of five. Clearly the relation connects a red/yellow necklace with a yellow/blue one. It also connects the yellow/blue one with a green/blue one. However, the relation does not connect the red/yellow necklace with the green/blue one, so these three necklaces do not form an equivalence class.

In an equivalence class, if A is related to B and B is related to C then A is related to C; we can show this:

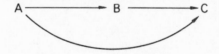

and with older children we should say the relation is *transitive*. Also in an equivalence relation, A is related to B and B is related to A. We call this *symmetric*:

Further, if we have only one blue block in a restricted universe, clearly this would be in an equivalence class of its own under the relation '... has the same colour as ...' At first sight it may seem a little strange, but this block is, of course, the same colour as itself. This relation is *reflexive*. Any likeness relation must be *reflexive*, but a difference relation never can be *reflexive* since A can never be different from A. We show a reflexive relation as:

In an equivalence relation all three of these are satisfied. Let us consider '... has the same colour as ...' on the following blocks:

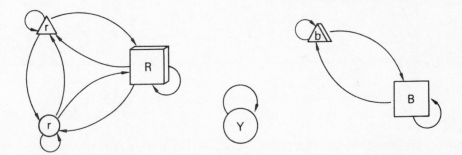

We see that arrows never travel from one equivalence class to another. This representation is called a *papygraph*.

Perhaps the most commonly met equivalence relations in elementary mathematics are '... has the same value as ...' or '... has the same number as ...' We use these relations to establish that 2 cows, 2 pencils, 2 motor cars belong to the two 'family' or 'club'. Later we use them to say that 2 of anything put with 3 of anything has the same number as 5 of anything; that is, $2+3 = 5$.

Yet again we use them to say that a £1 note has the same value as a 50p piece and five 10p pieces, and, as we shall see later, that $\frac{1}{2}$, $\frac{5}{10}$,

0.5, $\frac{17}{34}$, all belong to one equivalence class while $\frac{17}{35}$ belongs to another. Since this idea is so central to mathematics, it would seem pedagogically undesirable to restrict young children to experience of just one equivalence relation, $=$.

It is possible to use the equivalence classes established under an equivalence relation as a basis for other relation activities.

The arrangements of blocks which arise from the relation '... is the same colour and shape as ...' might look like the following:

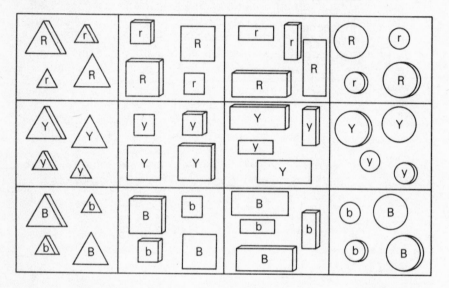

If a block is now selected from one equivalence class, say ⟨B⟩, a one

difference domino game can be played using the rule that only one piece may be used from each equivalence class.

It will quickly be seen that under these rules only blocks of one size and thickness will be used. Other versions of this game are possible: for example, four differences between adjacent blocks.

 etc. etc.

7   A View of Number

Readers will no doubt be wondering why it is taking so long to reach the familiar ideas of number which have, up to now, occupied such a central role in mathematics teaching. In this chapter we shall study some of the problems which surround the learning of number and show how some of our lines of development so far will facilitate the process.

We should not, of course, confuse the ideas of number (that is, what is meant by five, 5, V, cinq, and so on, however we write it) and the ideas of notation which help us to economise in writing the number. (We shall look at notation in Chapter 9.) The way in which number work is normally presented to children denies the existence of these two sets of ideas, so one task in teaching should be to repair this omission.

Let us take a cool adult look at the basic ideas involved in number, so we can shape the activities for the children in a way which will convey these ideas most effectively.

Firstly, we need to understand that just as red can be the property of a logic block (or set of logic blocks), five can be the property of a set of things. Just as red is not a property particular to one single logic block, but a property we deduce by seeing many blocks (and things) which are red, five is not a property of a particular single set, but a property we deduce by seeing many sets with this property in common. This means that just as we formed equivalence classes under the relation '. . . is the same colour as . . .' on the universe of logic blocks, we can form equivalence classes under the relation '. . . has the same number as . . .' on the universe of disjoint sets. Five is an abstract idea, and in the same way that one cannot describe red to a person who has never had the gift of sight, one cannot describe the idea of five without giving examples of it.

Our experience of five is extensive, but to a child not always helpful. For example, five sweets, five toy cars, or five minutes are apparently similar, but the latter has a transitory characteristic not possessed by the others, in that you cannot *see* all the minutes in a line like the cars or sweets. If we include with these the number 5 bus, house number 5, we have an even wider range of applications. Numbers surround us, indeed bombard us, in our daily living, but it is easy for a child to remain semi-permanently in a state of pure counting and never really come to understand the ideas behind the numbers.

To deal with numbers in arithmetic, we must fully understand their *cardinal* properties (the 'how many?' ideas). We must see clearly the place of equivalence, and make use of one-to-one correspondence as a test for equivalence in number. This is, of course, what children do when they say 'one for you, one for me . . .' when sharing sweets. However, if you ask the children if they both have the same number they will often not know without counting. This is because they confuse 'having the same number' with needing to know 'how many'.

Next we should understand the order properties of number, to see that four is less than seven but greater than two. Now, four is less than seven because if we take as many sets of four things as we please, we can put them into one-to-one correspondence with one another, likewise with as many sets of seven things as we please. These form two *equivalence classes*, because we have applied a relation '. . . has the same number as . . .' each time we have used the idea of one-to-one correspondence. However, we are unable to put any set from the four family into a one-to-one correspondence with a set from the seven family. Hence we know that four is always different from seven. Further, we can deduce readily that seven is more than four, because we 'use up' the things in the set from the four family while there are some left in the set from the seven family when we attempt the one-to-one correspondence.

However, this is not the complete picture, since we also have the idea of 'the next one', which is concerned with succession. How are we to identify the fact that the number following four is five? Suppose we begin with the equivalence class of all sets containing the smallest possible number of items (other than zero). This will, of course, be one. We know that these sets:

all belong to the same equivalence class because we can use the one-to-one correspondence test. Let us take a single set which will represent this family called one.

Now let us make another set which also belongs to the same family, and alter it in the simplest way possible, so that it no longer belongs to the same family. If we are not to return to the empty set, this will be:

How did we make this alteration? Simply by putting in *one more*. This new set does not belong to the same equivalence class as our collection above (because there is no one-to-one correspondence between this set and the others). However, there are plenty of sets which can be put into one-to-one correspondence with it; these make up the two family.

Now we are ready to modify the typical set again; we can remove one item, but this returns us to our one family. Alternatively we can put in another item and this becomes typical of the three family. So the sequence builds up by considering representative sets from each equivalence class and modifying them by means of the one more operator.

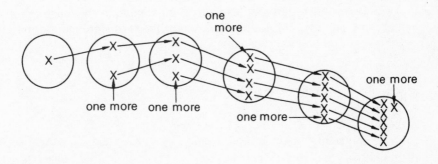

This process can go on for as long as we wish, generating the sequence called the natural numbers. Later we shall see how we learn to write these numbers.

8 Order Relations

Multi-criteria ordering

We have met simple order relations in earlier chapters; these have been mainly of the kind '. . . is heavier than . . .', or '. . . is worth more than . . .', and so on. There is really a great deal more to the idea of order than this.

Suppose we consider the situation of a class of children waiting to leave the room at playtime. To make the departure orderly it is decided that girls should *always* leave before boys. This only partly solves the problem since 20 boys can still make a fair job of jamming a doorway. So another rule is introduced: this is that shorter children leave before their taller fellows. Suppose now that two children approach the door wishing to leave the classroom, who should go first? Clearly we cannot say unless we have some information about the children. What would be the most useful thing to know, (a) their sexes, or (b) their relative heights? A moment's reflection on the statement above will show that one must first know the sexes; if they are different then the girl goes first even though she may be a 10 stone, 5 ft 6 in. Amazon, and the boy a 3 stone midget. However, should the sexes turn out to be the same, then we should need to know the relative heights.

Clearly then, we *must* know first the piece of information about relative sex, and we *may* need to know the relative heights. We see that our criteria for ordering have different levels of significance. In this case the sex is the more significant criterion, the height the less significant criterion.

For any two children we ask:

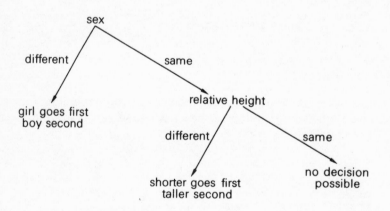

Of course, all this is quite arbitrary and there is no reason why it should not be reversed, letting little children go before bigger ones unless two are the same height, when the girl goes before the boy.

This is perhaps not the best example for the start of children's experience, although, of course, there is no reason why this cannot be considered later with the other experiences described below.

Road/Tree diagrams

These provide a very good model from which the multi-criteria ordering ideas can be developed. Let us consider the following diagram:

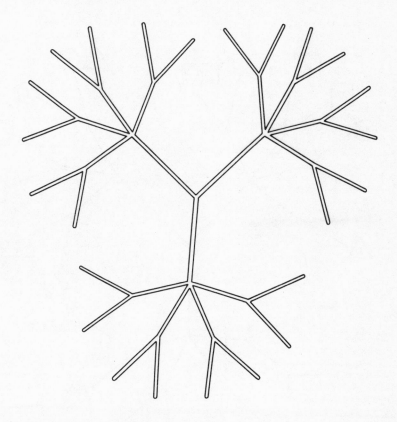

To go with this we shall use all the logic blocks of one size (suppose we take all 24 small pieces). These would be given to the children in a random form, inviting them to place one block at the end of each branch (or road) so that there is some pattern in the arrangement and so that the arrangement is tidy.

It is not difficult to see that there are three major sections to the road system, and it might be sensible to assign blocks of one colour to each of these major sections. Within each of these major sections there is a further division into four parts and we could place blocks of the same shape together in these subsections. Finally, each of these subsections has a further pair of subsections which would accommodate the different thicknesses sensibly. Now all that remains is to make sure that we are consistent in placing the blocks in the subsections on the different parts of the system. The final result might look like this.

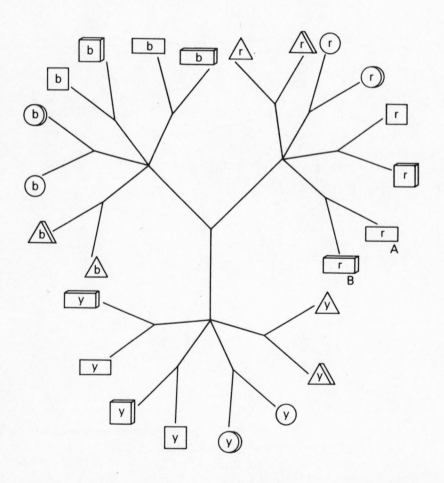

It is not difficult to see that this arrangement is consistent and takes note of all the attributes of the blocks. The sequence of shapes is always

 etc.

wherever one starts, and the blocks are always thin-thick-thin-thick. (Notice that there are not the same number of differences between adjacent pieces, although there is always at least one difference.)

If we were to interchange the blocks marked A and B, the blocks would still be ordered with reference to colour and shape but not thickness. This latter arrangement would not be *wrong*, since there can be no *wrong* and *right* in this situation. All we can say is that some arrangements are better than others.

The road system illustrated is described as being 3×4×2 because it divides in three ways at the first junction in the centre, four ways at the next set of junctions, and two ways at the final set. Of course we can rearrange the blocks to be in a different colour order, or a different shape order, or a different thickness order.

If we look at the roads leading from the centre, we see that each leads to blocks of one colour, at the next junction we see that each of the roads leads to a particular shape, and finally to a particular thickness. We can summarise this as follows:

At first junctions   roads lead to   red

yellow

blue

At second junctions   roads lead to

At third junctions   roads lead to   thin

thick

We could even label the roads as follows:

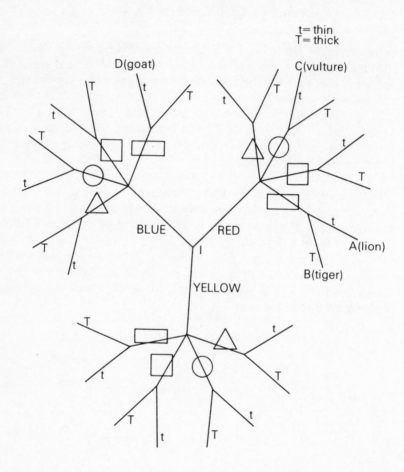

t= thin
T= thick

Now we can play the Zoo game (either with or without the labels). Suppose the entrance to the Zoo is at I and the animals live in enclosures at the end of the roads labelled by our logic blocks. We wish to visit the lion, how do we find him? The guide tells us to go down the *red road*, then down the *rectangle road* and finally down the *thin road*. Suppose we made a mistake and went along the *thick road*, we would come to the tiger. He is a fine beast but not the lion we were looking for—how do we correct our mistake?

58

This is simply done by returning one junction and correcting the final direction. However, if the mistake had been made in the 'shape' direction, and we had arrived at the vulture by mistake, this error would need a longer walk to correct it since we would have to go back two junctions. But even worse would be a mistake in colour, say blue for red. In this case we should arrive at the goat and the only way we could correct this error would be to go back to the entrance and begin again. Clearly some information is more significant than others and in this case it is colour followed by shape followed by thickness. (How does this relate to our earlier discussion about the children in the classroom?) It does not matter how we move the blocks around in this road system, the hierarchy of significance will be the same.

How can we change this hierarchy? This can be done by redesigning the road system.

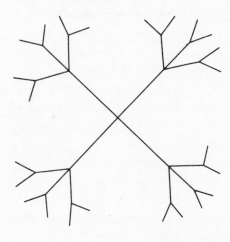

Now the hierarchy of significance becomes shape (most important), then colour, and finally thickness. The reader can easily design the other four road systems which will give all the possible different hierarchies.

Although many young children are well able to deal with this situation without the need for a long sequence of introductory steps (the so-called 'deep-end principle'), others may be helped by first encountering a system in which there are only two criteria, say 12 blocks (3 colours and

4 shapes) on the road system below.

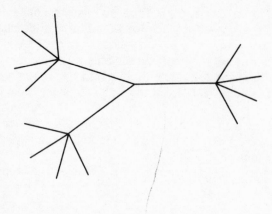

It is possible to design a road system in which some (or all) of the criteria can be interchanged without difficulty. Consider the following case:

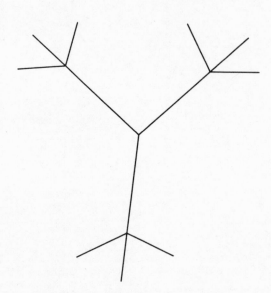

Using 9 blocks of 3 colours and 3 shapes, clearly we could make either shape or colour the first criterion and the other the second. So two essentially different arrangements could be the following:

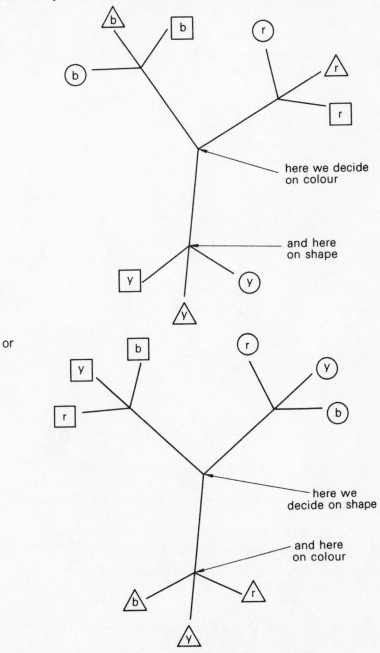

or

here we decide
on colour

and here
on shape

here we
decide on shape

and here
on colour

In Chapter 4, pages 36–8, there was an explanation of how to construct the systems of sets materials. These can, of course, be used in all the relations activities described earlier. Here we shall explain in some detail how these are applied in the ordering activities described above.

Let us suppose we have a set of cards exactly like those described on page 38. The discriminating attributes were

    Variable A: 0, 1, 2, or 3 soldiers
    Variable B: no animal, a dog, or a horse
    Variable C: button or no button

Let us now try to arrange them on the road system (3×4×2) with which we started this section.

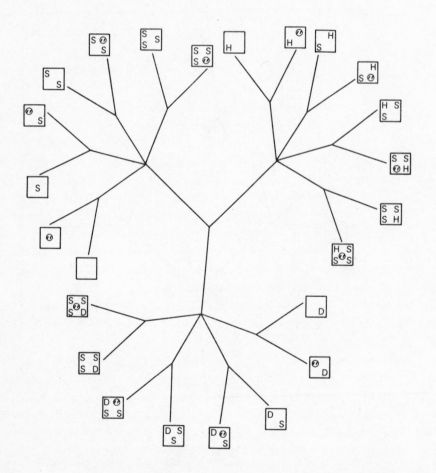

'Dictionaries'

Having completed this, the lively mind is likely to wonder if there is not a connection between the cards used on this occasion and the blocks used previously. There is certainly one card for each block, for instance card $\boxed{s}$ is where the block $\textbf{b}$ was before.

The reader should be able to work out the following dictionary, which will enable a block to be translated into a card, no matter where it occurs on the road system.

block	card
SHAPE △ ○ □ ▭	SOLDIERS none one two three
COLOUR red yellow blue	ANIMALS horse dog none
THICKNESS thin thick	BUTTON none one

So a square which is red and thin will be in the same place as a card with two soldiers, a horse and no button.

Clearly many such dictionaries are possible, depending on the ways in which the blocks and cards are placed on the tree. We could have put the horse with the yellow blocks, the dog with the reds and no animal with the blues. Similarly, the no soldier cards could have been put with

the rectangles, the one soldier card with the triangles, and so on. However,   SHAPE   must always relate to   SOLDIERS,
                COLOUR   must always relate to   ANIMALS,
           THICKNESS must always relate to   BUTTON,
since the four values of the shape variable cannot be matched with only
three values of the animal variable.

Other representations for ordering activities

Naturally it would be very dangerous for the children to believe that
ordering games can only be played on these road systems. So we must
introduce some other kinds of games. There is space for only a brief
description of them, but exactly the same principles apply as have been
described above.

Lattices

(a)

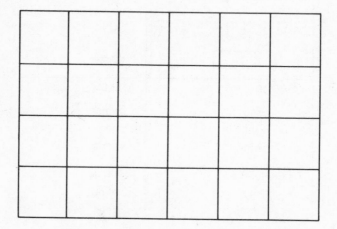

This is a 6×4 lattice, which is probably best used as a 4×3×2 lattice
with a similar collection of material as that described earlier in this
chapter (page 55). The task is to place one block in each space so that
there is some pattern in the arrangement and so that the arrangement is
tidy. Clearly the best arrangements will again take note of all these
variables. An arrangement might look as follows:

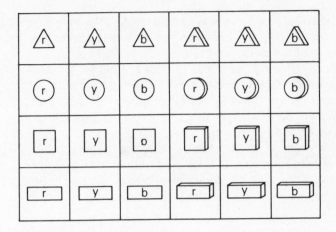

Dictionaries can be formed as before.

(b)

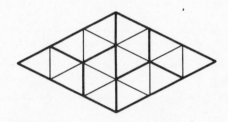

Again the same idea of the rectangular lattice is used. $2 \times 3 \times 3$ systems are needed in this version.

Circle diagrams

The hardest—generally!
  This consists of
a $2 \times 2 \times 2 \times 2$ circle
diagram made
from a hoop and
some card strips.

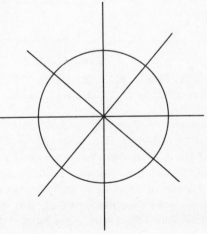

The sixteen compartments should be filled with blocks of 2 shapes, 2 colours, 2 sizes, and 2 thicknesses. There should be a system about the placing of the piece relative to all these attributes.

Without removing these pieces, place a set of 16 people pieces in the diagram (2 colours, adults and children, sitting and standing, male and female). Then create a suitable system of sets, each time trying to associate the new attributes with the attributes of the other sets. (This is also a good problem for a road/tree diagram.)

It is possible to use the equivalence classes established under an equivalence relation as a basis for other relation activities. We can, of course, begin with the equivalence classes we met in Chapter 6, page 50. The equivalence classes can be ordered by arranging the sets of blocks in line:

red triangles
red squares
red circles
red rectangles
blue triangles
blue squares
blue circles
blue rectangles
yellow triangles
yellow squares
yellow circles
yellow rectangles

The blocks within the classes can now be ordered by putting large blocks first and small ones second, and within this arrangement thick before thin.

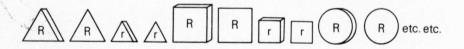

Within this ordering, it is possible to detect that some parts of the information are more important than other parts. Suppose two blocks are chosen at random and we wish to discover which is nearer to the left-hand end of our arrangement. If the blocks are different colours, say red and blue, we need no other information to determine the order of the two blocks. However, if the colours are the same we now need to know about the shapes as well. Should these be the same, the next most significant information concerns the size. The thickness can only be used if all other attributes of the two blocks are alike.

Applications of multi-criteria ordering

This work, while intellectually demanding in itself, is designed as a lead into situations which will make a great deal of use of these ideas. This will be developed in the following chapter. Before we leave this section, however, let us look at one commonplace situation in which we need to make use of these ideas.

Suppose we are looking for the word CAT in the dictionary. On our first attempt we find DOG. CAT precedes this because C comes before D in the alphabet and we disregard the remaining letters. Now we find COT; again CAT comes before this (the initial letter is the same, but the second letter comes after that in the desired word). Now we find CAP; the first two letters are the same, but the last letter comes before that in the desired word, so CAT is after CAP. Finally we find the desired word. It would be a more tedious task if we were to look for OPERATE in the same way but the principles are the same and they depend upon working out the hierarchy of significance in ordering criteria: we order by the first letters, and then by the second, and so on.

9   Understanding Notation

In Chapter 7 we considered some of the ideas which need to be understood if one is to have a clear view of number. Now let us look to see what are the important ideas which are necessary to understand notation.

It is one thing to have established the sequence of numbers (found the sequence generated by the 'one more' property described in Chapter 7). It is quite another to write the number down.

× ×

The number of crosses in the line above is invariant even if we do not know how many there are. We start the recording of the small numbers we count by introducing new number names and symbols for each in turn—one (1), two (2), three (3), four (4), and so on. Sooner or later one is forced into some form of economy in writing; we cannot produce hundreds of names and expect to remember each of them, or to remember the sequence without error. So we use a system of grouping. It is well known that our system of grouping numbers is based on ten, but of course in the imperial system of weights and measures the grouping is based on a variety of numbers.

The Romans used a grouping system and they had special symbols for five (V), ten (X), fifty (L), hundred (C), etc. By combining these symbols it is possible to write large numbers in compact form. One thousand nine hundred and seventy one is one thousand and one hundred less than another thousand, together with fifty, twenty and one i.e. MCMLXXI. This system is very cumbersome for computation, but this is not surprising since it was really designed for recording.

Try adding MCMLXXI+MDCCXLIV and you will see the difficulties.

Our number system relies on the ingenious idea of place value. We use 0 as 'place keeper' when we have no number in a particular position. 205 and 25 are quite different because the 0 indicates 'no tens' in the first number.

Let us look at the number 5708: this means

5 thousand + 7 hundred + 0 tens + 8 units

or 5×1000 + 7×100 + 0×10 + 8×1

Of course, 100 and 1000 are multiples of ten, so we could use an index notation to write the number.

$$5 \times 10^3 \; + \; 7 \times 10^2 \; + \; 0 \times 10^1 \; + \; 8 \times 1$$

Also 1 can be expressed as a power of 10, i.e. 10^0, so we get

$$5 \times 10^3 \; + \; 7 \times 10^2 \; + \; 0 \times 10^1 \; + \; 8 \times 10^0$$

Now look at each part. We can see that each of them is composed of three parts:

(a) the digits (marked ↗) which appeared in the concise original number;

(b) the base or grouping number (marked ↑) which indicates the size of groupings (ten) we are using;

(c) the index or power (marked ↙) which shows the number of successive times that we have grouped in tens.

There is clearly no reason why each of these cannot vary so, in general terms, each number is composed of parts of the form $d \times b^p$, and the number itself is the sum of such parts.

It is not really desirable to introduce these ideas to children in this way. However, to give the children as complete an understanding as possible of the ideas of notation, it would seem to be a good thing for them to *see* base and power varied as well as the digits.

Traditional teaching overtly varies the digits, disguisedly varies the powers, and rarely (if ever) varies the base.

10   Grouping Games

The idea of grouping

As stated in Chapter 9, there must come a time in counting when the objects are grouped and we start to count the number of groups. To understand the idea of grouping we make groupings of natural objects which are too large in number to be counted by the simple numbers up to 9. What we need to do is to find a number for the club to which these larger sets belong. It may be relatively easy to understand the idea of 5 or even 9 if the child sees enough examples of sets belonging to the clubs. This does not imply an understanding of numbers like 12, since the additional problem of notation has complicated the situation.

The normal way of grouping in our number system is by tens. This is not because ten is essentially easier than any other system, but merely the accident that the human body has ten fingers. It is not difficult to see that had we all been endowed with eight fingers, we should have accepted grouping by eights as quite natural. It is suggested that children might get a better understanding of the idea of notation if other groupings (or bases, as they are called) are used. To a child there is no difference between twelve and nine as counting numbers, but when they are written as 12 and 9 we make use of the idea of grouping and recording the numbers by means of place values.

Let us consider grouping the fish below. Suppose we are only able to count up to three, so our groupings must be done in threes. When we find that there are more than three groups of three, these will have to be grouped again into 'super groups' and so on.

Children will need a lot of experience of these ideas in the practical situation.

Introductory grouping activities

Take a handful of small toys (or beads or pegs) which we wish to count. Of course we could just count them in base ten as usual, but instead let us explore the way in which we can count them by grouping in different ways. Suppose we first establish sets of three as far as possible, by making loops around them, perhaps using string, or drawing a line with a felt pen. All the toys may be inside loops, but it is very likely that some (either one or two) will be left as they are not enough to form another set of three. For example:

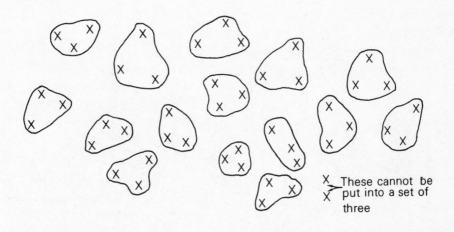

X These cannot be
X put into a set of
three

Now we can group together our sets into sets of three. We should use a different colour for this second grouping.

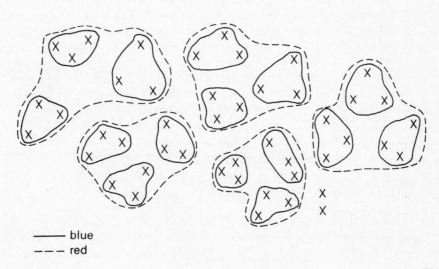

———— blue
– – – red

In the example above, all the first grouping sets are regrouped a second time; clearly there could have been either one or two of these first groupings left over (that is, they might not have formed a second grouping).

This process could be repeated as many times as necessary; in the example we are considering there is one further grouping possible.

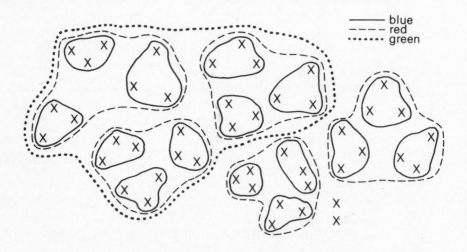

—————— blue
— — — red
·········· green

Now we need to find out how many we have altogether. We should count how many sets we have formed with the largest grouping used; in the example above, there is just one set of the third grouping. Now we must look at the next lower grouping; in our example, there are two sets of second groupings. We proceed similarly through the groupings in turn. In our example, there are no first groupings which did not get included in the larger groupings, and finally there are two singles (or ungrouped objects). So the number of objects is

3rd grouping	2nd grouping	1st grouping	singles
(green)	(red)	(blue)	
1	2	0	2

GROUPING GAMES

In this way we have found the number of toys (say) in base three. The process could be repeated in a different base.

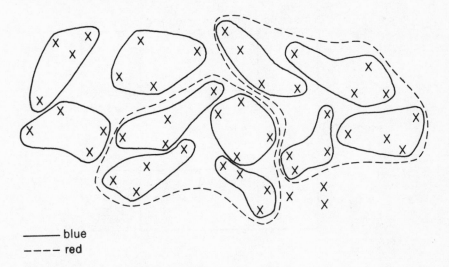

——— blue
- - - - red

The number of objects (which is, of course, the same as before) can now be written in base four as

2nd grouping	1st grouping	singles
(red)	(blue)	
2	3	3

The idea of grouping can be developed in another way by using a card with, say, a number of fish.

Place a cube on each fish and then move all the cubes to a sheet of paper marked out as shown below.

3rd grouping	2nd grouping	1st grouping	singles

The successive grouping is shown below.

			singles

Using either interlocking cubes or the Dienes Multibase Arithmetic Blocks (M.A.B.),* this yields:

		1st grouping	singles

This is followed by:

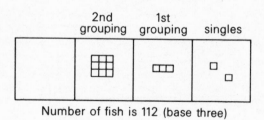

2nd grouping	1st grouping	singles

Number of fish is 112 (base three)

---

* Dienes Multibase Arithmetic Blocks are obtainable from ESA Creative Learning Limited.

GROUPING GAMES

It is, of course, possible to combine two such groupings. Suppose we have two 'fish' cards and we wish to see how many fish there are altogether. Combining these groupings is the process we call addition, and might look like the following.

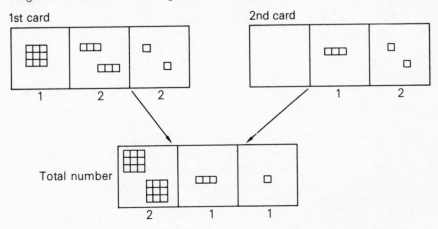

When the ideas of grouping have been developed further we shall look at the other operators which are normally associated with arithmetic.

Another valuable activity is the grouping of a quantity of material in one base and then regrouping it in another base; thus we see the same quantity expressed in a different notation. For example,

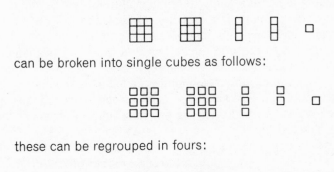

can be broken into single cubes as follows:

these can be regrouped in fours:

A second grouping in fours produces:

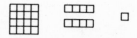

The island game is a useful extension of these ideas. Briefly, a magician controls the islands under a certain rule. On Three Island, if there are fewer than three people, they must live in separate caravans, but any group of three must live in a bungalow; however, any groups of three groups of three must live in a three-storey house, and so on. Animals have to be grouped in the same way. The story can be embroidered if necessary; for example, let all the people and animals travel to Four Island, where all the above laws operate with the 'rule of four' instead of the 'rule of three'. In this way the people and animals can be counted again in a different base.

The use of Multibase materials

The Dienes Multibase Arithmetic Blocks (M.A.B.) mentioned on page 74 provide a valuable aid to the study of notation through the variation of base. The drawing on page 1 shows the composition of sets of the original material, now called rectangular M.A.B. It will be seen that each piece is related to the unit cube. The first grouping (sometimes called a 'long') is formed by joining the appropriate number of unit cubes into a stick. The second grouping (sometimes called a 'flat') is formed by laying the first grouping pieces side by side, and since the second grouping uses the same base as the first grouping, these new pieces are necessarily squares. The third grouping (sometimes called a 'block') is formed from the second grouping pieces piled up into a cube. For smaller bases this process is continued further into fourth and higher grouping.

Since it is felt that it is very undesirable for the learner to see only one embodiment, other multibase material has been constructed to represent the idea in a different way. The triangular and trapezoidal material illustrated below makes use of different groupings of triangles. For those readers used to the terms unit, long, flat, and block, it is perhaps worth mentioning that these descriptive terms are not appropriate to the triangular material, while the more arithmetical expressions, first grouping, second grouping, and so on, apply just as well in this case, and, in fact, to any other embodiment we might wish to use.

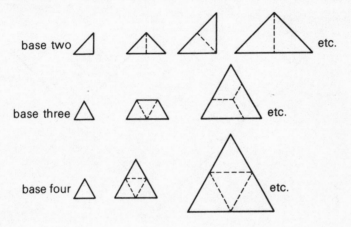

11   Ordinal Aspects of Number
Significance in ordering

In Chapter 8 we looked in some detail at the use of tree diagrams for ordering relations. The next stage of development from the tree diagrams of the previous work is the organisation of these into a fan-like shape.

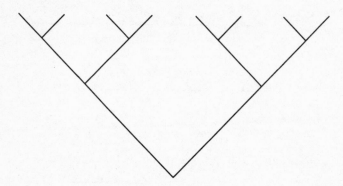

This now concentrates on the linear type of order and draws more attention to the limbs of the tree/roads.

Suppose we used a 2×2×2 system of logic blocks comprising 2 thicknesses, 2 colours, 2 shapes, which we arrange sensibly on the tree; such an arrangement might be this one.

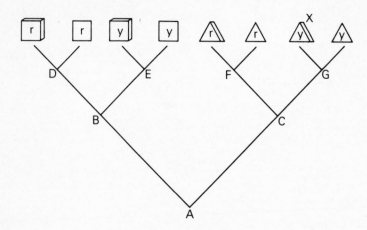

We can now begin to discuss how we arrive at any given block by following the roads.

Let us recall how we would reach the block marked X by traversing the roads starting at A. We need first to choose a road from A; we could say right or left, but perhaps it would be better to name the road, and roads are often named by the place to which they lead. Clearly, the road from A must be the 'triangle' road. When we get to C we have another decision to make, to follow the 'yellow' road, and at G we must take the 'thick' road. A sensible 'address' for the X block would be 'triangle-yellow-thick'. The order in this sequence is vital, since an instruction to proceed along the 'yellow' road from A is meaningless. Clearly, therefore, the 'triangle' part is the most significant. Notice how an error in a more significant instruction is more serious than in a less significant one. By saying 'thin' instead of 'thick' you are near the correct place; saying 'rectangle' for 'triangle' puts you in quite the wrong part of the road system.

We could develop the idea of giving directions in the form of instruction to go left or right at each junction. So to reach X we should say 'go right at the shape junction, right at the second junction, and left at the third', or just 'right, right, left'. So $\overrightarrow{RRL}$ gives the address in a different form. Here we see that the information given by the 'string' $\overrightarrow{RRL}$ becomes less significant as we read along the 'string'. Notice that the address is completely changed if we alter the order in the 'string'; for example, $\overrightarrow{LRR}$ is very different from $\overrightarrow{RRL}$. This helps us to see why 711 is different from 117!

Systems of sets made from multibase material

We have already seen how we can use the systems of sets described in Chapter 4 for ordering activities on tree diagrams (Chapter 8). When the children are familiar with these ideas and understand how sets can have properties in the same way that objects can (through playing the dictionary games, for example), we should introduce sets with more abstract properties. The properties we shall now look at concern the groupings which were discussed in the last chapter.

We begin by laying out a set of cards and, using M.A.B. material in base three, we arrange the cards so that each one is different from the others.

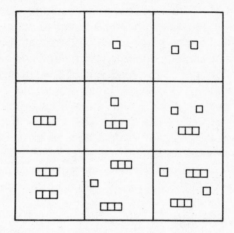

If the reader can forget for a moment about counting the cubes in base ten, it will be seen that we have constructed a 3×3 system. Each card has either no unit cube, one unit cube, or two unit cubes as one variable, and as the other variable either no 'stick', one 'stick', or two 'sticks'. Thus any card can be different from another in one or both of these two variables.

Suppose now we arrange these cards on a tree

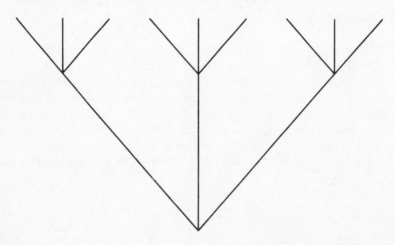

and to the instructions for producing a tidy arrangement we add, 'Make the card on the left have the least wood, and make sure that every other card has more wood than any on its left.' The card with most wood should now appear on the right. We see that the more significant limbs of the tree distinguish between cards with differences in the number of sticks or first groupings. The less significant limbs only distinguish between the number of units on the cards.

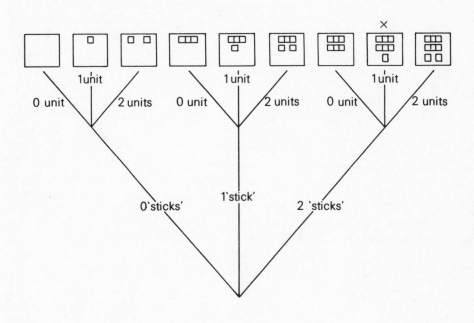

The card marked X can be reached by traversing the '2 sticks' road, followed by the '1 unit' road. Hence the address can be written as 21 base three.

To see this more clearly, we should look at a set of twenty seven cards made in a similar way but incorporating second grouping pieces as a third variable, and placing the cards on a 3×3×3 tree (see the next illustration).

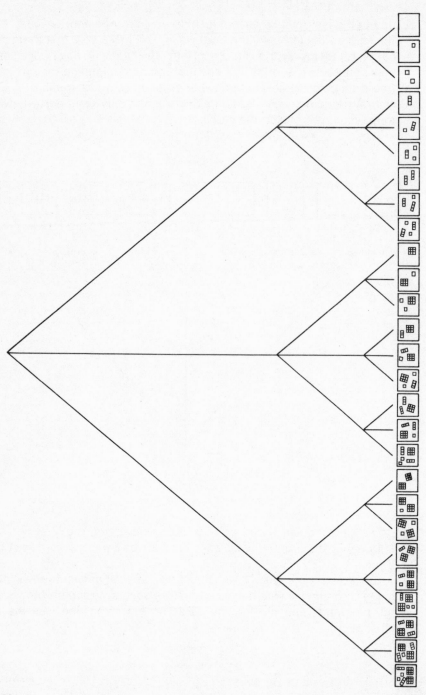

12 The Basic Operations of Arithmetic using Multibase Materials

Operators on the ordered set of cards on the tree

We have already seen how the early grouping activities with multibase materials readily lead into the ideas of addition, although these are not in any way formalised. It is not difficult to extend our earlier ideas on machine (that is, state-operator) activities to provide a lead towards these formal processes.

Let us return for a moment to the tree/road situation with base three M.A.B. illustrated in the previous chapter. The reader will recall that this arrangement was established by reference to the ordering of sets of sets of material with an additional condition of 'more wood to the right'. We can now use the arrangement of these cards on the tree in conjunction with some operators. Some of the most important basic operators are one more, two more, one less, and so on. Suppose we have operator arrows like these:

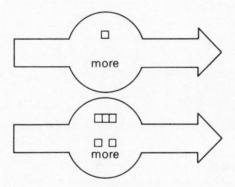

We can select a card (from not too near the right hand end of the tree) and associate the operator with it:

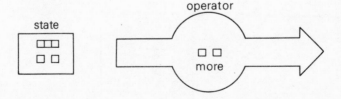

By using a suitable collection of base three M.A.B. it is possible to find the output of the machine which has been thus established. This output must be one of the cards from the tree and must therefore be

because no other card has the correct quantity of wood on it.

We can now examine the pattern which arises from associating the operator with different states, and also the successive application of an operator to a specific state. This will generally resolve itself into two different kinds of activity.

Firstly, an initial state is chosen, an operator is applied to this, so establishing a final state. This activity will be repeated a number of times using the same operator until the child realises that there seems to be a pattern. In this case, the final state is chosen with reference to the initial state; for example, using the pattern 'next but one to the right' always produces

than the initial state (in the base three tree on page 82).

Machines

Picking out cards from the tree diagram to satisfy the operator arrows is not quite the same situation as exploring the state-operator-state idea in general. For example, the cards exhibit only possible combinations of material in base three and there is therefore no card with

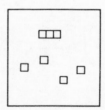

However, the machine problem
  base three

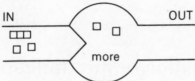

could produce such an answer for the unwary. It is necessary, therefore, to consider many such operators and to establish the need for meaningful outputs in relation to the material.

All early work on machines should utilise a format like the one above. However, for later work, and for simplicity in this book, we shall use the following style, indicating at the same time the base to be used.

base three

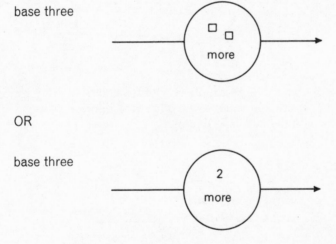

OR

base three

There are two basic 'one input' operators, the addition (and subtraction) and the transformation or multiplication operators. Little more need be said about additive operators as applied to natural or counting numbers, except that

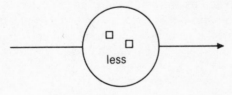

cannot operate on an initial state of □. There is no way in which we can subtract 2 from 1 using the natural (or counting) numbers. In order to do so, it is necessary to extend the number system to include the *integers* (which unfortunately is outside the scope of the present book).

Transformation or multiplication operators

These operators have their roots in the early activities with the logic blocks.

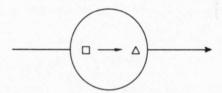

Suppose now we have a large supply of squares and triangles (or other similar material) in which the pieces are otherwise identical. We can still use a machine with the following operator:

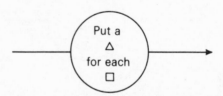

With this material we cannot match a *particular* output piece with any given input piece as we could with the logic blocks. However, we can observe if there are either not enough or too many output pieces. So in effect the machine establishes a one-to-one correspondence by number between the input and output sets:

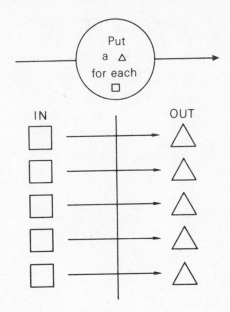

It is only a little step to use a set of rectangular strips instead of the triangles, so we now have an operator like the following:

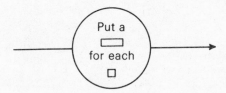

Since this appears to be an operator which increases the quantity of wood, it can be further developed in two ways using M.A.B., either (a) by putting several cubes for each one in the input, or (b) changing the rectangular strip shown above into a first grouping in M.A.B. It is, of course, necessary for the child to have had ample experience in the grouping games described earlier before he can progress to the stage of working or indeed recording in symbol form.

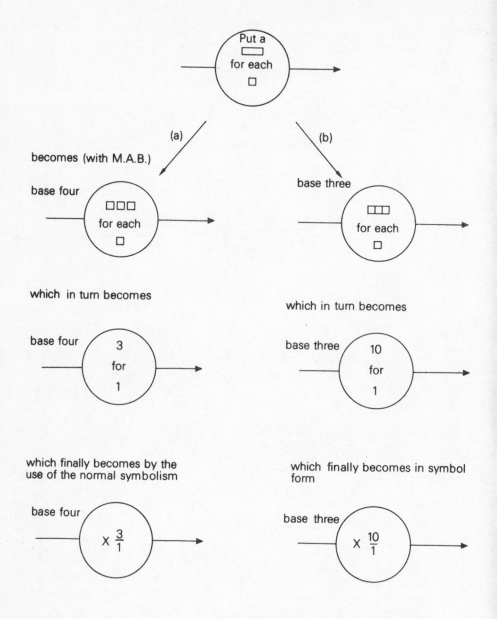

Let us consider further the work from the point at which the M.A.B. is introduced. We can use a recording sheet developed from the input/output tables (see page 28).

BASIC OPERATIONS USING MULTIBASE MATERIALS

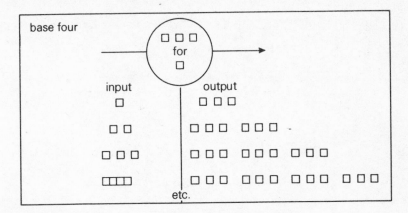

This should of course be regrouped in base four.

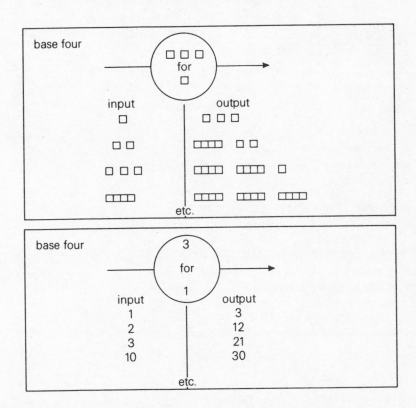

The reader will recognise the above as a 'three times' multiplication table written in base four.

These operators may also include more complex versions, for example:

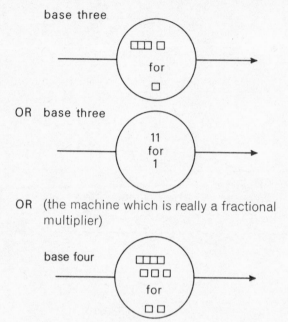

base three

OR base three

OR (the machine which is really a fractional multiplier)

base four

The last of these requires inputs which are multiples of 2. Since at this stage we can deal only with natural numbers, the fractions will have to come later from another view of the machine idea.

Two input machines

The machines we have considered so far use a fixed operator on a single input. We shall now consider a type of machine which has two independent inputs and combines them by some rule. Perhaps the simplest of these is the 'put together' or addition machine.

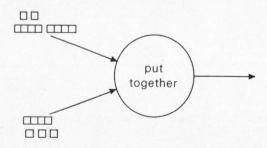

A replica of each input set is formed in turn in the output, using one-to-one correspondence.

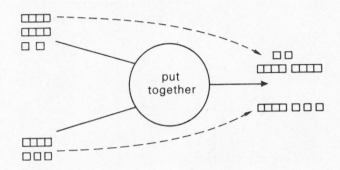

The output set should now be grouped if necessary.

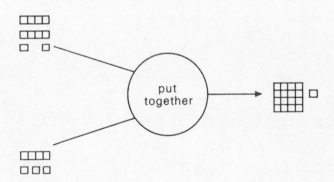

The advantage of this two-stage method is that it preserves the input sets for comparison with the final output. It also provides a model for the other operations we shall meet later.

In order to understand the processes of more formal computation it is necessary to see clearly the steps involved. Let us outline some of the steps which might be followed in looking at addition.

The activity shown above can be displayed using a modified version of the input/output table introduced earlier.

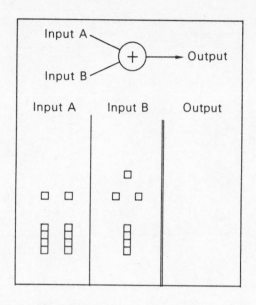

Both inputs are *copied* into the output column.

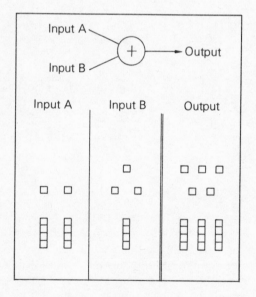

The ouput is now grouped (as before).

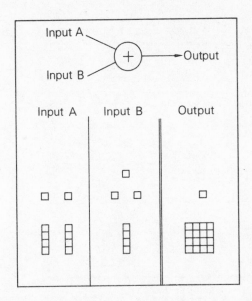

Since the original inputs A and B are preserved throughout, they can be compared with the final output.

A format of this kind can also be used as a basis for a recording sheet. At this stage the record would be in the picture form shown above.

More complex calculations can lead to extensive regrouping.

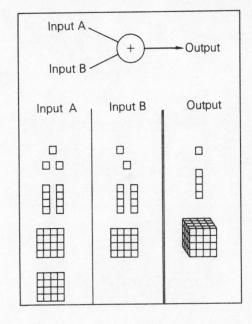

In this case it is more difficult to see the connection between inputs A and B and the final output.

However, by turning this sheet on its side as follows, we can 'lay out' the M.A.B. in a systematic way. The output set is again formed by copying each of the inputs A and B.

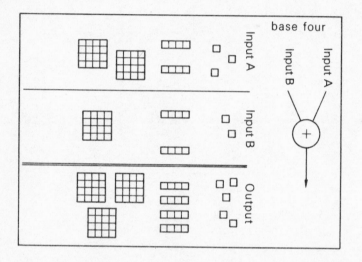

In this case we see more clearly that regrouping also involves changes in position.

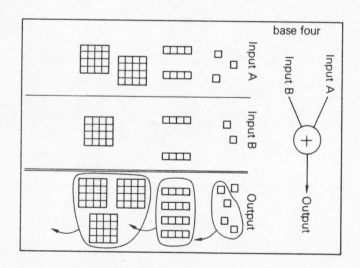

This gives us:

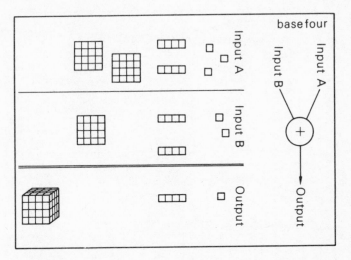

Eventually these ideas can be recorded in symbol form. There is no need to show the divisions on the various pieces so long as the base is clearly indicated.

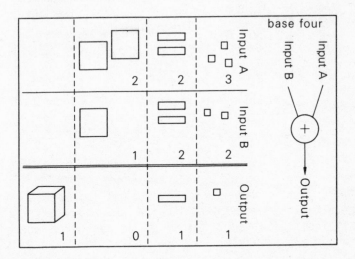

Here we see the importance of zero as a place holder.

A new recording sheet is probably an advantage at this stage.

Input A $\searrow$ $\textcircled{+}$ $\rightarrow$ Output Input B $\nearrow$ $b^6 \quad b^5 \quad b^4 \quad b^3 \quad b^2 \quad b^1 \quad b^0$	base....
	Input A
	Input B
	Output

It is possible to use a transition stage, with the following symbols instead of b^3, b^2, b^1, b^0,

but this method has disadvantages since it is a representation which is not really suitable for triangular and other versions of multibase material. Using this new recording sheet, we can now use numbers only.

Input A $\searrow$ $\textcircled{+}$ $\rightarrow$ Output Input B $\nearrow$ $b^6 \quad b^5 \quad b^4 \quad b^3 \quad b^2 \quad b^1 \quad b^0$					base four.
	2	1	2	2	Input A
	1	2	3	3	Input B
1	0	0	2	1	Output

At all stages it is important for the child to relate the recording with the manipulation of the actual materials. There is no value in forcing the child to use the material for longer than is necessary, and indeed he should be weaned away from it, if he appears to be clinging unnecessarily to the model. However, the teacher should use common sense in this, as premature and forced denial of the support of the material will destroy the benefit derived from the previous activities. Indeed, some children find it helpful to have a box of multibase material open on the table without actually touching it.

When the teacher feels that the child is secure in the recording described above, 'problems' can be set in which the child is given the base
to be used and inputs A and B. Using these, he finds the output (initially
it may be necessary for him to use the multibase materials). His ability to
establish the output without the material will depend upon his understanding of the steps he goes through in manipulating the blocks. The
teacher can help him to interpret this and assist in designing his recording to include such things as carrying figures (if these are helpful). In
this work there seems to be no case for progressing from so-called easy
to so-called difficult examples. The reader will observe that even the
earliest example above includes addition of three digit numbers complete with 'carrying' figures. This would hardly be possible if base ten
only is used because the numbers (or rather digits) can become so
large, and representations in base ten M.A.B. require so much wood,
that the structure is not as readily visible.

The steps described above take the pupil from the practical activity
exemplified by

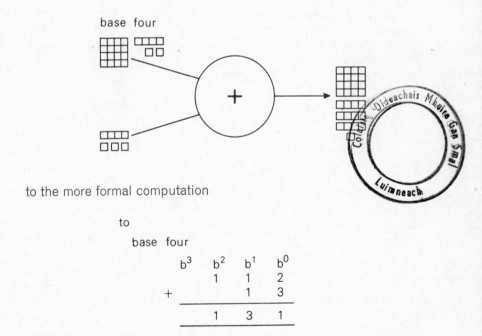

to the more formal computation

to

base four

b^3	b^2	b^1	b^0
	1	1	2
+		1	3
	1	3	1

but at *any stage* or *any time* in the future he can return to his original
model if he does not understand what he is trying to do.

Subtraction

Let us turn now to the ideas of subtraction. The steps already described will apply equally well in this case.

In subtraction we normally apply the convention that we subtract the quantity on the lower input from that on the upper. Alternatively, the machine can be used to find the difference between the quantities (in which case order is not important).

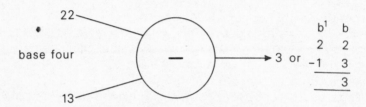

It should be noted that subtraction can arise in many different situations, for example, 'take away', 'how much more', 'difference between', and so on. Let us examine two of the most useful ways in which we might record these processes.

a) Decomposition

Let us consider the following machine:

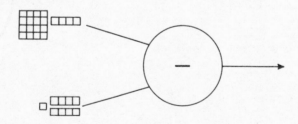

We copy the upper input set into the output as we did earlier (using the convention that we subtract the lower input from the upper). We now try to form within this new set in the output a subset which is like the lower input set. When this has been done, this subset is removed. Again it is possible to compare the input sets with the final output set. This process is called decomposition and the steps of the activities in the output set are shown below with the corresponding recording at the final stage:

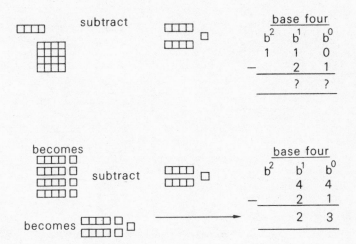

b) Complementary addition

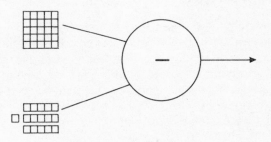

Alternatively we could copy the lower input set into the output and build it up until it becomes the same as the upper input set. We then remove from this new set the subset corresponding to the lower input. This process is again described below.

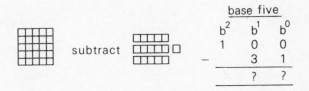

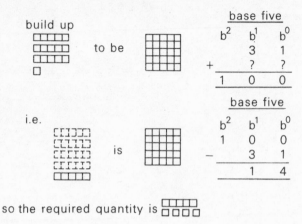

so the required quantity is

The latter method is frequently used by shopkeepers when finding the 'change' for a money transaction.

Multiplication

Multiplication in a two input machine can be considered as an operation in which we make a number of copies of one of the input sets (normally the bottom input set) in the output. The number of copies made is determined by the number of objects in the other input set. This relates very closely to the single input machine used earlier for multiplication, since this single input behaves in the same way as the upper input in the new machine. The activities described below do *not* lead immediately to the algorithm (process) known as long multiplication.

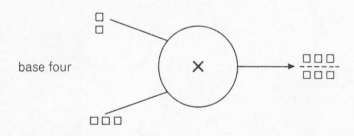

base four

which simplifies to,

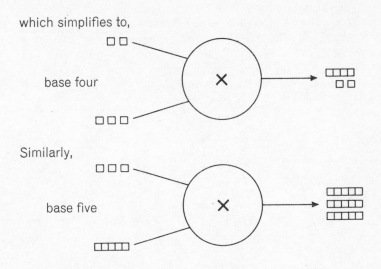

base four

Similarly,

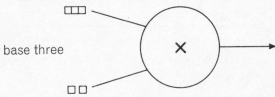

base five

If the upper input set contains a first grouping,

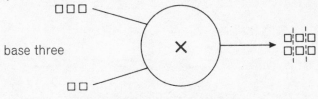

base three

it may be thought of as being composed of separate units,

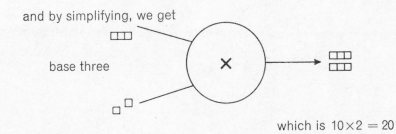

base three

and by simplifying, we get

base three

which is $10 \times 2 = 20$

The reader should also notice that this shows that
$x \times 2 = 2x$ where x can be regarded as any base number or any other unknown.
If both inputs include a first grouping,

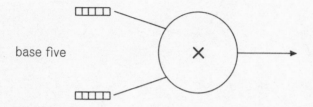

these can again be broken down as far as necessary.

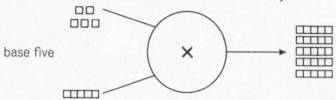

This when regrouped becomes

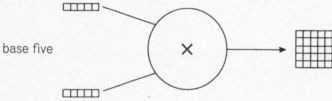

which is $10 \times 10 = 100$
This result is true for any base and can be read in general terms as
$$x \times x = x^2$$
There is, of course, no reason why we cannot have a second grouping in one or other of the inputs.

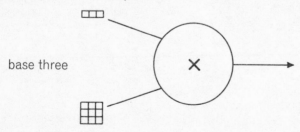

We can proceed by breaking down the upper input.

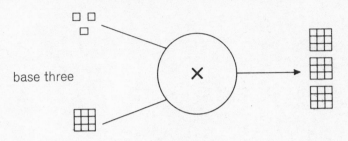

base three

Regrouping this becomes

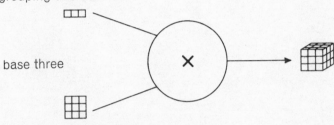

base three

i.e. $10 \times 100 = 1000$.

A more complex situation is given below:

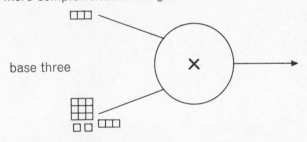

base three

The output, which can be formed by combining the ideas given in the preceding examples, will be

so $10 \times 112 = 1120$

or $x \times (x^2 + x + 2) = x^3 + x^2 + 2x$

However by the time we reach the case in which there are mixed pieces in both input sets, the problem has become almost too difficult to solve by this method.

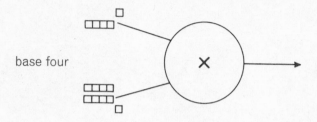

base four

We can resort to the earlier method of breaking down input A.

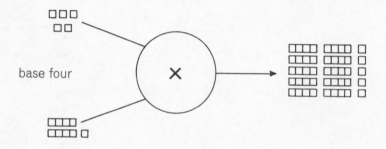

base four

Regrouping this gives

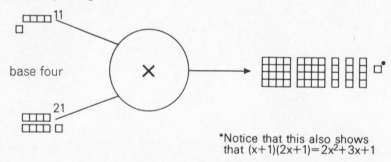

base four

*Notice that this also shows
that $(x+1)(2x+1) = 2x^2 + 3x + 1$

We shall return to this type of problem in the next chapter where we will look at ways of dealing with long multiplication.

Division

Before discussing the process of division, it is important to recognise that this can be of two kinds. To take a simple example: suppose we have a ribbon 1 metre in length. We can ask two types of division questions:

(i) How many pieces 10 cm long can be cut from it? This would be most easily solved by cutting off 10-cm pieces until no ribbon is left, and then counting up the pieces. We could describe this as *successive subtraction* or '*quotition*', because we know the *size* of shares we are to make and we wish to find out the *number* of shares.

(ii) How long will each piece be if we cut the ribbon into 4 parts? Most people would solve this problem by folding the ribbon in four and cutting at the folds. The length of each piece is then measured. This process is called '*partition*' since we know the *number* of shares and we now wish to find out the *size* of each share.

Let us look at these ideas using the machines. In the case of a single input machine we can see the idea of *partition*, for example:

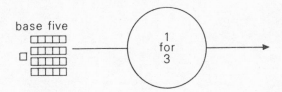

This can be read as 'make the input into 3 equal parts and make the output the same as one of these parts'.

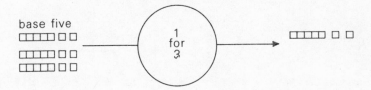

However, it is also possible to view this as *quotition* by reading the operator as 'put one cube in the output for every three cubes in the input', thus:

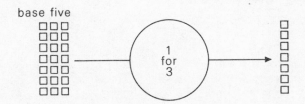

which when regrouped becomes

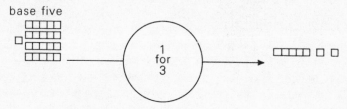

In the two input machine it is more natural to ask, 'How many sets like the one on the lower input can be made from the set on the upper input?' This is quotition, since we know the size of the share we want. We now need to find out how many shares we can make. Two examples are given below.

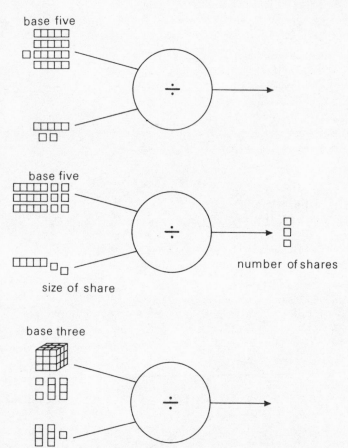

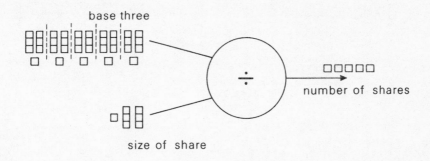

base three

number of shares

size of share

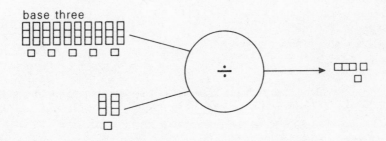

base three

With a little additional thought the reader may see that this result can be obtained by a rather shorter but more sophisticated process.

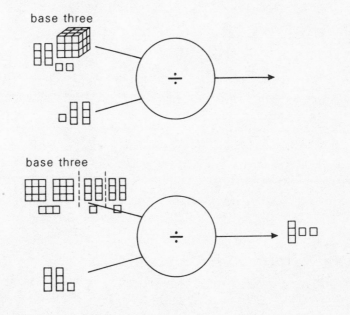

base three

base three

The significance of the ▭▭ in the output can be seen by considering the inverse operation of multiplication.

Since the product of ▭▭ with the second input $\left(\substack{\text{▯}\\\text{▯}}\ \substack{\text{▯}\\\text{▯}}\ \square\right)$ gives ⊞ ⊞ ▯

which is found in the first input.

This is summarised in the following machine.

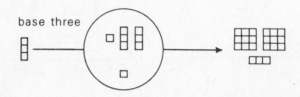

Of course, all the examples considered above are such that the division process leaves no 'remainder'. In general, a remainder is very likely to occur in situations other than those set up expressly to exclude it. Clearly if a remainder appears it must be acknowledged as such because at this stage there is no way in which fractional parts can be introduced into the output in a mathematically correct form.

13 Some Fundamental Laws of Arithmetic

Associative Law

Let us consider again chains of operators such as:

state—operator—state—operator—state

Using base ten arithmetic with an initial state of 3 (say)

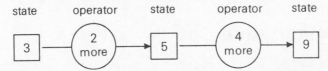

We might now look for a way of getting from the initial state of 3 to the final state of 9 by means of a single operator which can be shown as:

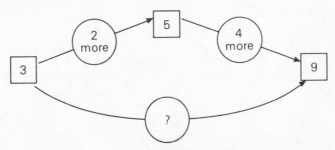

We are seeking a way of transforming a state of 3 into a state of 9; this could be either a 'x 3' or '6 more' operator. Now we should try a different input—2, say, giving a final output of 8. Immediately it can be seen that the 'x$\frac{3}{1}$' operator is no longer valid, but the '6 more' operator is still a suitable replacement. This single operator is, therefore, a replacement for a *chain* of two operators. Naturally children will need to explore many similar situations using multibase materials.

We may now ask if this replacement is dependent on, or independent of, the initial state and final state. Clearly, it is independent of these states and we have a useful rule of arithmetic. So we can say that:

$$(3+2) \qquad +4 \quad \text{(initial chain)}$$
$$= \quad 3 \quad + \quad (2+4) \quad \text{(replacement operator)}$$

We call this the *associative law* of arithmetic addition.

The corresponding law in multiplication is illustrated as follows:

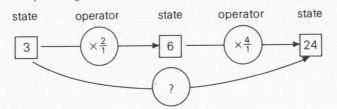

The replacement operator is $\times \frac{8}{1}$
So we can say that
$\quad\quad\quad (3\times2)\times4$ (initial chain)
$\quad\quad = \quad 3 \;\times(2\times4)$ (replacement operator)
(Are there corresponding laws for subtraction and division?)

Commutative Law

If we have two initial states we can combine them with a 'put together' machine.

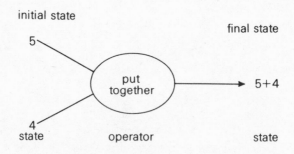

$\quad\quad\quad\quad 5 \quad\quad\quad$ put together with 4 $\quad\quad\quad 5+4$
This could be re-stated as:
$\quad\quad\quad\quad$ *state* $\quad\quad\quad\quad$ *operator* $\quad\quad\quad\quad$ *state*
$\quad\quad\quad\quad 4 \quad\quad\quad$ put together with 5 $\quad\quad\quad 4+5$
So we have the *commutative law* for addition: $5+4 = 4+5$
   A similar law exists for multiplication, but not for subtraction and division (since, for example, $5\div4 \neq 4\div5$).

Distributive Law

In an earlier chapter we looked at two kinds of operators:
one input (a) the additive (or subtractive) kind, for example, 2 more, 121 more (base four), 35 less (base six), etc.
$\quad\quad\quad\quad$ (b) the multiplicative (or divisive) kind, for example, 2 for 1, 4 for 3, 2 for 5 (base six), etc.
and
two input Put together (for example)

What happens if we meet the multiplicative and 'put together' operators in the same chain?

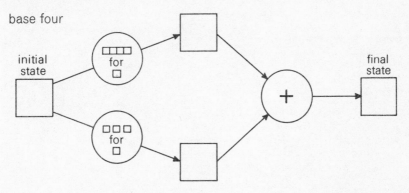

Let us use a small input, say ☐ ☐, and follow through the machines on the upper and lower tracks:

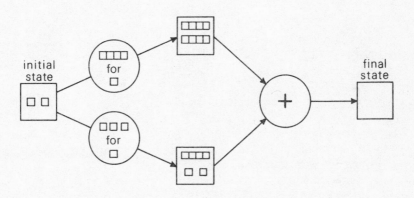

The final stage in the 'put together' machine produces this result:

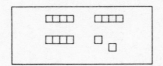

So we can now ask ourselves what the replacement operator might be.

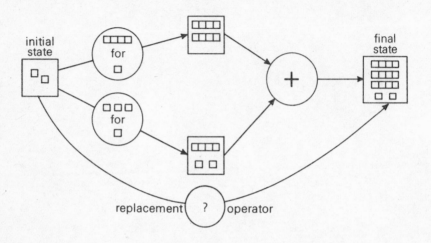

At first sight this could be

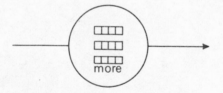

but if we change the initial state the operator will also need to be changed. However, if we use the operator

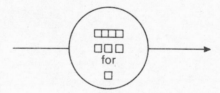

we can change the initial input as much as we like but this single operator will still be satisfactory. Readers will see the connection between the original operators A and B, and the replacement operator.

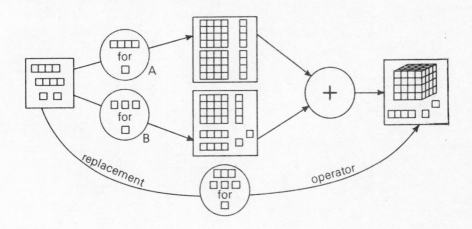

The checking of the replacement operator is not at all easy, which brings us to the reason for considering this elaborate machine. If the replacement operator is difficult to use and the more complex machine is easier, we have a device for dealing with multiplying by mixed quantities like 13 (base four).

In fact this machine shows us how to deal with long multiplication. Let us suppose we wish to evaluate the following.

base five

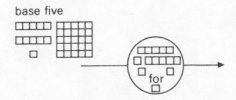

We can break down the operator and produce the new machine.

base five

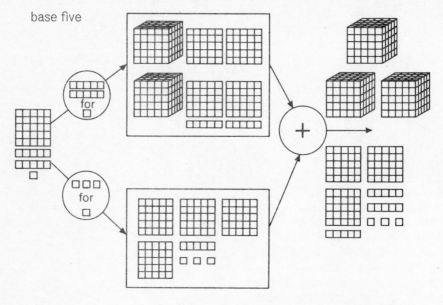

This can be described in number form.

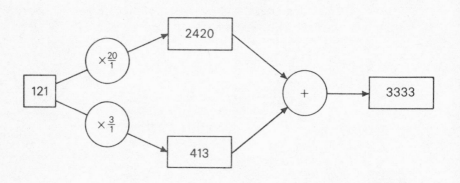

We can immediately see the long multiplication algorithm.

	b³	b²	b¹	b⁰
base five				
		1	2	1
×			2	3
1st machine	2	4	2	0
2nd machine		4	1	3
Put together machine	3	3	3	3

Three-digit multipliers can be treated in a similar manner. Adequate work with M.A.B. should precede the written stage.

base three

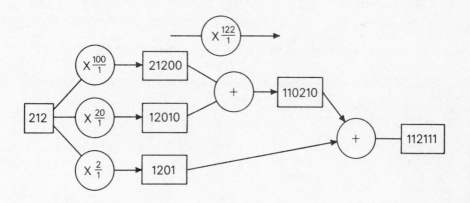

This can be written concisely in the following way:

base three	b⁵	b⁴	b³	b²	b¹	b⁰
				2	1	2
×				1	2	2
1st machine		2	1	2	0	0
2nd machine		1	2	0	1	0
3rd machine			1	2	0	1
	1	1	2	1	1	1

Let us summarise these ideas in base ten arithmetic.

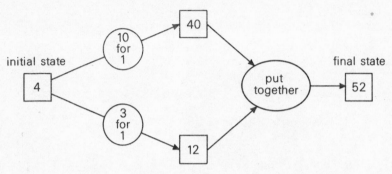

As before, we are looking for a single operator to take us from the initial state to the final state. At first sight '48 more' would do, but this is dependent on the states. However, '13 for 1' will always work irrespective of the initial state/final state.

In conventional notation, we are saying that in ordinary (i.e. base ten) arithmetic:

$$(4 \times 10) + (4 \times 3) = 40 + 12 = 52$$

with replacement operator

$$4 \times 13 = 52$$

We are using the *distributive law*. This law is implied every time we use the process known as 'long' multiplication.

$$\begin{aligned} 27 \times 13 &= 27 \times 10 + 27 \times 3 \\ &= 270 + 81 \\ &= 351 \end{aligned}$$

this is summarised in the algorithm:

$$\begin{array}{r} 27 \\ \times\ 13 \\ \hline 270 \\ +\ 81 \\ \hline 351 \\ \hline \end{array}$$

For the operations of arithmetic we say that *multiplication is distributive over addition*.

It is very important to notice that we cannot apply this rule in the 'reverse' kind of way.

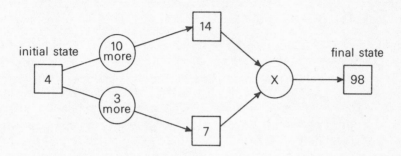

Neither '$\times \frac{49}{2}$' nor '94 more' will do as a single replacement operator as both of these prove to be dependent on the initial state. The reason for this is perhaps more clearly seen in the generalised situation:

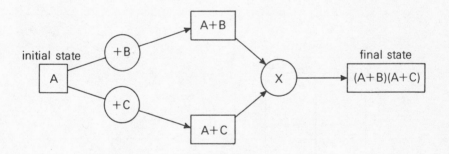

in which the final state involves a component of A multiplied by itself and is therefore dependent on the initial state A.

All three of these laws are fundamental in arithmetic and the algebra of numbers, but we shall not expect these laws to be true in other mathematical systems. Many very useful systems exist which are not commutative.

Section II Sets and Logic

14   Logic Statements and Set Statements

Sorting

In the first section of the book we have seen how material can be sorted into sets by considering the various attributes of the objects being sorted. For example, if we consider the sexes of the children in a class we are easily able to sort them into two sets, 'boys' and 'girls'. Of course, no children are left over because if a child is not a boy then that child must be a girl. However, if we were to sort them into sets of those wearing sandals and those wearing shoes, it is at least possible that there will be some children who can join neither set (perhaps because they are wearing boots, or are barefoot). So we come to realise that it is easier to sort objects into sets on the simple basis of whether they possess an attribute or not.

The reader will recall that we showed several ways of doing this. The two most interesting are perhaps the Carroll diagram and the decision tree. These have been labelled to take logic blocks.

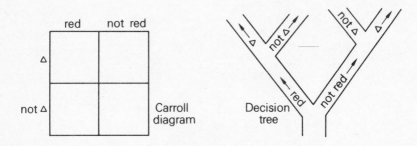

Each object is *sorted* by considering each *attribute* in turn (seen very clearly in the decision tree) and as a result of this sorting the object joins a *set*. It is important to realise, however, from this early stage, that the things we say about connecting attributes (which are logic statements) and the things we can say about connections between sets are different although related statements. Let us explore further.

Conjunction and Intersection

We shall start by combining a decision tree and a Carroll diagram.

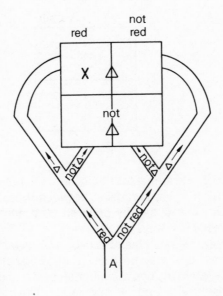

Each block enters at A. It passes along the appropriate roads and arrives in the Carroll diagram to join other members of the same set. Let us see how a block can arrive at X. It must have the attribute of being red *and* it must also have the attribute of being triangular. Of course it must be both of these things so we can make the simple *logic* statement that 'it is both red and triangular'. We call this kind of 'and' statement a *conjunction*.

If we now look at the sets in the Carroll diagram, we see that our object belongs to the set of red things at the same time as belonging to the set of triangles. This is more simply described by the statement: 'The intersection of the set of red blocks with the set of triangles.'

So the logic statement tells us about the attributes of the object, and the corresponding set statement tells us about the set to which it belongs.

Disjunction and Union

The distinction between logic statements and set statements is even more apparent in the following diagram.

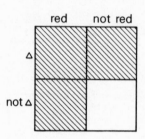

How are we to describe the logic and set properties related to the shaded region? It is the confusion between these that causes many of the difficulties experienced by children (and adults) in describing the situation correctly.

One frequently hears statements like, 'We have all the reds and all the triangles.' While this may be true, it is not exactly helpful, since it is neither a set statement nor a logic statement, and it causes confusion with the precise use of 'and' we had earlier. The correct *set* statement is, of course, 'The union of the set of red blocks with the set of triangles.'

We can establish the corresponding *logic* statement by examining the various routes on the decision tree which lead into the three shaded regions. It is easily seen that any block which passes along the *red* road must arrive in the desired region. It is also true that any block which travelled along either of the triangle roads is in the desired region. Therefore the 'successful' block must have *either* the attribute of being red *or* it must have the attribute of being triangular. So our logic statement becomes, 'it is either red or triangular'. We call this kind of 'or' statement a *disjunction*.

There is a further problem in the use of the word 'or'. Frequently the word 'or' is used in everyday language to mean 'one or other but not both' ('I do not know if I shall go to Spain or Italy for my holiday this year' is generally interpreted in this way). In logic terms we describe this as '*exclusive disjunction*' (exclusive or), and although this is by no means universal, we usually use these terms to describe such a situation. A Carroll diagram showing the positions of blocks with the property of being 'either red or triangular but not both' is shown below.

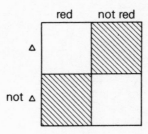

The corresponding set statement is frequently described as the symmetric difference of the set of red blocks with the set of triangles.

When children are familiar with the attributes of the material (whatever kind we may choose), they should be encouraged to describe in *set* language the regions filled in the Carroll diagram (or Venn diagram) and in logic the connection between the attributes possessed by the material which produced these sets. For example:

(a)

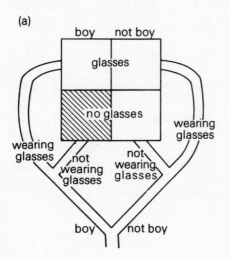

Set statement
The intersection of the set of boys with the set of those children not wearing glasses
Logic statement
Each child is both a boy and not wearing glasses

(b)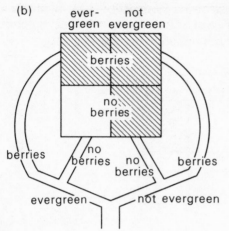

Set statement
The union of the set of plants which are not evergreens with the set of plants that have berries
Logic statement
Each plant is either not evergreen or it has berries

Implication

The last example leads us to consider an alternative logic statement which produces the same set situation. Suppose we remove anything which is in the unshaded region of the Carroll diagram. Let us consider again the paths that lead to occupied regions of the Carroll diagram. If we go down the 'evergreen' road then we must also go down the 'berries' road if we wish to find any objects. Briefly this says, '*If* the plant is evergreen *then* it has berries.' This is a conditional statement or an implication. Notice that this statement tells us nothing about any plant that is *not* evergreen, which *may* or *may not* have berries. Let us look at this in a slightly different way. Firstly we sort the blocks as was done on page 119. Then we erect a barrier across one of the paths.

Let us consider which blocks can be reached if we start at the entrance and go down the roads which are open to us. It is not too difficult to see that the three regions which are accessible are collectively described as the union of 'the set of not reds with the set of triangles'. The corresponding logic statement is 'each block is either not red or a triangle'.

However, there are other statements that can be made about this situation:

If the block is red *then* it must be . . .

Clearly it must be *triangular* since this is the only possible route after entering the red road.

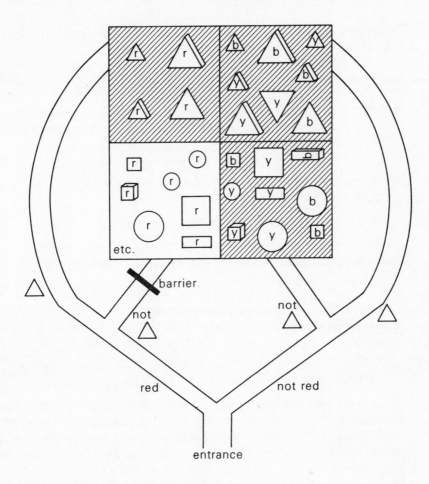

So one new statement is (briefly):

If red *then* triangular.

Notice that nothing is said about what happens when the block is *not* red since either triangles or not triangles are accessible from the *not* red road. So we see that the statement

If red *then* triangular

means also that should the block be *not red* it can be any shape.
It is a common mistake to believe that the statement:

If red *then* triangular

means also *If not* red *then not* triangular.

This more rigid condition (explained below) is certainly not contained in the simple 'if . . . then . . .' expression.

So the statement:

If it rains tonight *then* I shall wash my hair

tells the listener only what I shall do in the case of rain; should it not rain I am completely free to wash my hair or not as the fancy takes me.

The statement

If red *then* triangular

is not the only 'if . . . then . . .' kind of statement that can be made. Suppose we start the other way round and say:

If not triangular then . . .

Clearly the missing words are NOT RED, because the only not triangles that can be reached are also not red. As before, the statement:

If not triangular then not red

means also that a triangle can be any colour.

Let us collect together the statements that can be made about this situation.

If red then triangular	If *not* triangular then *not* red
Either *not* red or triangular	Either triangular or *not* red

Notice the pairs of 'if . . . then . . .' and 'either . . . or . . .' expressions which are at the same time true, and it can be seen that by negating the first operand in the implication statement red → not red (or not △ → △), we can replace the 'if . . . then . . .' expression by an 'either . . . or . . .', or vice versa.

So:

	If	A	then	B
becomes	Either not	A	or	B
which is the same as	Either	B	or not	A
which can become	If not	B then not A		

Returning to the hair washing conditions:

	If rain then hairwash
becomes	Either not rain or hairwash
which is the same as	Either hairwash or not rain
which can become	If not hairwash then not rain

I am sure the reader will have more difficulty in accepting the last set of statements than the ones above. This is because it deals with everyday things and we add subjective judgments to the words people use when they make 'if . . . then . . .' statements. A rather clearer example of the sense of this kind of connective might be, 'If I buy a new car then I shall need an overdraft.' It could still happen that the overdraft is needed without the new car. and this agrees with the alternative possibilities listed above.

There are many imaginative games that can be played in the classroom based on these ideas. For example, we can ask the children to sort the logic blocks, people pieces, or other material by means of a suitable decision tree, then introduce the idea of a lion (or some other wild animal) which is sitting in the roadway leading to one of the sets of blocks in the Carroll diagram. We can then discuss which blocks can be reached in safety. This will lead to all the 'either . . . or . . .' and 'if . . . then . . .' possibilities described above. We can, of course, move the lion to different positions and so describe a whole range of new situations.

Double implication or equivalence

For completeness we should also consider the '. . . if and only if . . .' condition. On the decision tree we had earlier it will be necessary to erect two barriers. The only blocks accessible in this new situation will be the red triangles or the not red not triangles.

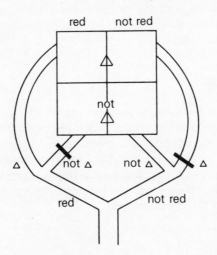

These correspond to the statement 'Red if and only if triangular.'

This is, of course, the conjunction of the two statements:

If red then triangular *and* If triangular then red,

or, alternatively,

If red then triangular *and* If *not* red then *not* triangular
(the reader should have little difficulty in establishing that these two expressions mean the same thing).

Remembering what was said earlier about the correspondence between 'either ... or ...' and 'if ... then ...', the statement

If red then triangular *and* If triangular then red

can be written as

Either not red or triangular *and* Either not triangular or red.

An alternative description would be

Either (both red and triangular) *or* (both not red and not triangular)

(again the reader might try to establish that this is a correct statement).

Notice that this latter statement is the one used when clarifying the exclusive disjunction statement:

Either not red or not triangular—but not both of these things.

Clearly then, the equivalence connective and the exclusive disjunction offer different ways of making the same statement. Both represent a stronger condition than the simple implication or disjunction but not as strong as conjunction.

Negation

We have used the idea of negation quite freely in the foregoing text. We should establish the link between the logic statement and set statements as we have done in the other cases. Suppose we sort our blocks into reds and not reds on a decision tree. If we retain the reds we can call this the output set, and if we discard the not reds we might call this the *complement* set. Hence *not* in the logic statement corresponds with *complement* in the set statement.

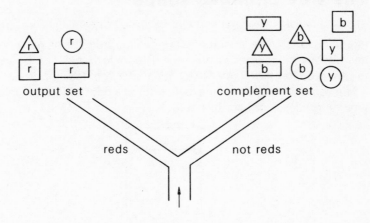

Summary of Logic and Set Statements

	Logic Statement	Set Statement
negation	not . . .	complement
conjunction	both . . . and . . .	intersection of set of . . . with set of . . .
disjunction	either . . . or . . .	} union of set of . . . with set of . . .
condition	if not . . . then . . .	
exclusive disjunction	either . . . or . . . but not both either both A and B or both not A and not B	} symmetric difference of set of . . . with set of . . .
equivalence	. . . if and only if . . .	

15　Logic Tracks

The tree changes shape

We have at our disposal another powerful method for developing the foregoing ideas. The logic tracks are derived from the decision tree which has already been used extensively. The logic tracks can be introduced to young children (6–7-year-olds) soon after the decision tree.

The basic component of the logic track is a gate which carries a mandatory instruction label, for example

These are placed across a track along which the blocks are passed. The blocks can only travel in the direction of the arrows and must enter on the right. A block having the attribute shown must pass through the gate, all others must not pass through.

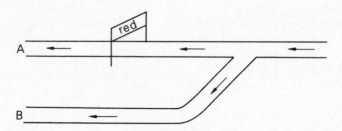

Clearly all the red blocks arrive at A and the 'not red' ones at B. If a further selection gate is now attached to these outputs, we have:

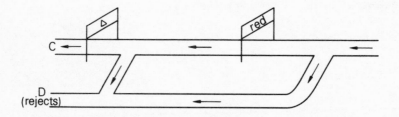

Any block arriving at C must be 'both red and triangular'. These blocks form the output set which is the 'intersection of the set of red blocks with the set of triangles'. We shall adopt the convention that the rejects are always on the lower track. This set is, of course, the complement of

the output set, and each block which is in the complement set has the attributes which are the negation of both red and triangular.

It can easily be seen how this derives from a decision tree, as follows:

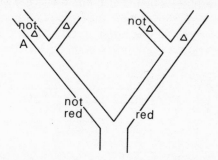

We are rejecting all not reds in this case so there is no need to sort the not reds at A, producing a modified tree.

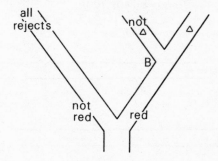

Similarly any block arriving at B is a reject so these blocks may join the other rejects.

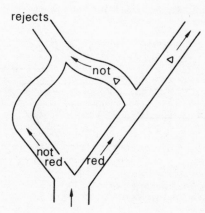

This is now topologically equivalent to the track with the gates shown earlier in this section (page 128). The only real difference lies in the labels. There appears to be some advantage in using this method of labelling (rather like signposts on a real road) with very young children before using the slightly more sophisticated gate mentioned above.

If a gate is moved to the lower track at a decision point, the blocks selected on the upper track become those with the negation of the attribute.

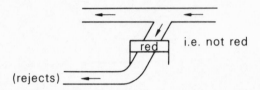

If we move one of the gates in the earlier track, each block arriving at C will be both not triangular and red.

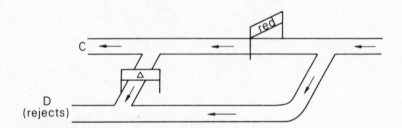

It is often helpful to place a Carroll diagram at the end of the track to receive the output set. It can be shaded to show the region(s) which will be occupied by blocks after they have passed through the gates.

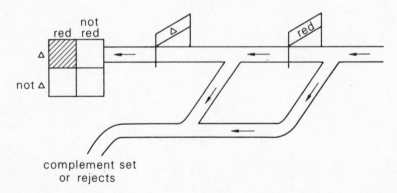

Early classroom activities

Experience has shown that the early activities can be usefully explored by the children sorting themselves on decision trees or logic tracks painted (or chalked) on the hall floor or playground. This gives them the opportunity of sensing the movement along the paths, the need to make each single decision in turn and to find a final destination.

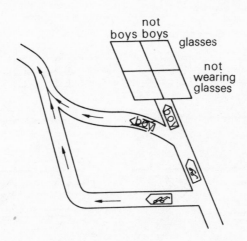

When the children have satisfied themselves of the output set derived from the configuration given, they should explore the different ways in which the labels (or gates) can be placed on the track.

To discuss this in detail let us return to the example given on page 130. To simplify the representation let us use a single line for the track —————— and a rectangular box for the gate

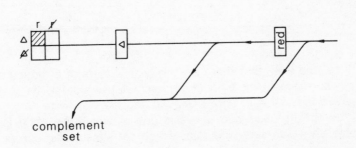

The children soon realise that a gate can only be placed after a fork, and after each fork there must be a gate. Since one attribute only can appear on any label, combinations of attributes must be obtained by further forks and gates. The gates must be placed in such a way that all blocks reach either the output set or its complement. Most children understand the common sense of this quite easily after a little discussion, particularly if one uses the familiar one way street situation as a model.

It is soon realised that there are in fact eight possible arrangements with the track layout.

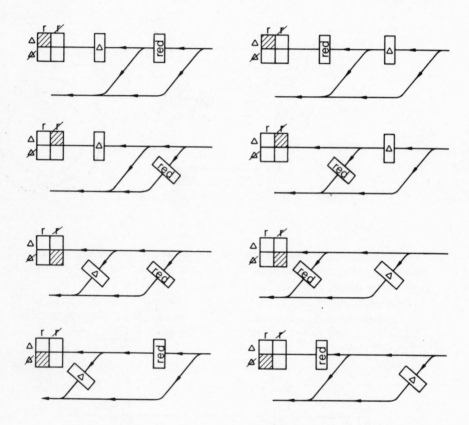

It can be seen that there are really four pairs of arrangements, each pair representing the equivalent commutative statements such as both red *and* triangular, or both *triangular* and *red*.

The activity described above is one in which the child is trying to establish which sets (and later which set statements) correspond with various different logic combinations. This can, of course, be reversed and we can ask the child to place the gates so that only a certain region of the Carroll diagram is filled. Here is an example:

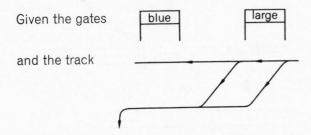

Given the gates

and the track

fill this part of the Carroll diagram.

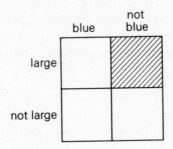

The two possible arrangements are shown below.

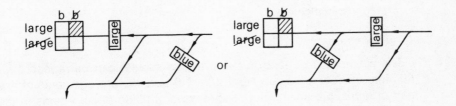

or

A suitable logic statement to describe this situation is:

'Each block is both large and not blue.'

The corresponding set statement about the output set is:

'The intersection of the set of large blocks with the set of not blues.'

133

Logic tracks and disjunction of attributes

It is possible to use other kinds of track layout.
e.g.

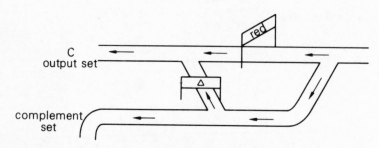

In this case all red blocks arrive at C, be they triangles or not, but also the triangles which are not red will arrive at C. A moment's thought will reveal that the blocks arriving at C will be *either* triangular *or* red.

If a Carroll diagram is placed to receive the output set, we see that three regions are filled.

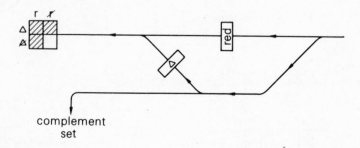

The activities described in the previous section can be repeated for this track. There are again eight different possible arrangements of this pair of gates, producing all possible ways of filling three regions in the Carroll diagram.

In a similar way the children can be asked to place the gates on the track so that certain regions are filled in the Carroll diagram.
For example,

place the gates   [blue]   [O]

on the track

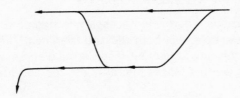

so that these parts of the diagram are filled.

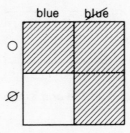

One possible solution is shown below.

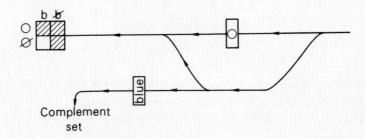

This arrangement can be described by the logic statement:

'Each block is either circular or blue.'

However, it can also be described by the statement:

'If a block is blue then it is circular.'

So it is not surprising that we have the same type of track for the 'if . . .
then . . .' condition. (See Chapter 14, pages 122–5.)

Negation and logic tracks

There are occasions when it is necessary to negate a combined logic statement, for example, '*not* both red and triangular'. Let us investigate the meaning of this new statement. The Carroll diagram which shows the region in which we find blocks that are both red and triangular is given below.

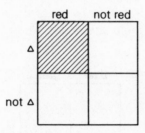

So any block which is *not* both red and triangular will be found in one of the other regions.

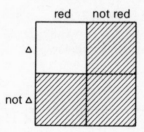

In terms of the logic tracks we need to reject the blocks which were in the former output set and accept those blocks which were in the complement set. This is achieved by the simple device of a 'not crossover'.

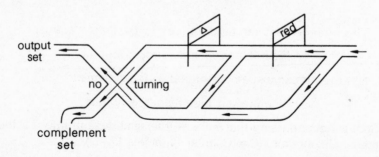

The logic track which represents

'not either not red or not triangular'

can be formed in a similar way.

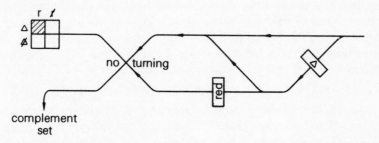

The reader may notice that the output set in this case is the same as that obtained under the logic condition 'both red and triangular'.

So we have two logic statements:

(a) not either not red or not triangular;
(b) both red and triangular;

which are equivalent (or belong to the same equivalence class) under the relation '. . . produces the same output as . . .'

The equivalence of these expressions demonstrates the truth of a part of De Morgan's Theorem.

16   Notation and Deduction

Notation

When the children have become familiar with the activities of the decision trees and tracks, and can describe the situations in words, they will begin to find a need for a symbol system which will represent what is happening. There are a number of possible ways of developing a symbol system to represent the logic ideas we have discussed in the preceding pages. One of the most interesting is derived from Lukasiewicz and is often called the Polish Notation. This notation uses one unary operator and several simple binary operators to cover the logic connectives, as follows:

N to indicate	not . . .	(unary operator)
K to indicate	both . . . and . . .	(binary operator)
A to indicate	either . . . or . . .	(binary operator)
C to indicate	if . . . then . . .	(binary operator)
E to indicate	. . . if and only if . . .	(binary operator)

Each of these operators precedes the operands to which it is applied. So,

both blue and triangular is written as $Kb\triangle$

not red   is written as Nr

if not yellow then $\bigcirc$ is written as $CNy\bigcirc$

It will readily be seen that the abbreviated notation is read from left to right, just as the phrase in words is read. No brackets are needed since all operators are either unary or binary and must act on the operands, or operand 'packages', that immediately follow them. So we read, where l means 'large',

$$K\,r\,A\,N\,\triangle\,\ell$$

as *both* r *and* $AN\triangle\ell$ since $AN\triangle\ell$ is a single operand package; this becomes

both r and *either* $N\triangle$ or ℓ since $N\triangle$ is a single operand package; which is

both red and either not triangular or large.

Below we see a track which selects blocks that are

both not triangular and red

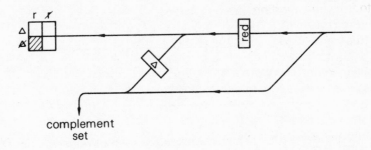

In Polish notation this is KNΔr.
In the following track,

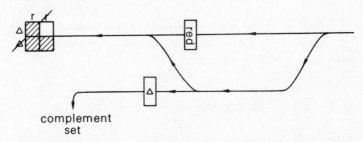

each block that arrives in the output set is either not triangular or red,
i.e. ANΔr.

By studying the arrangement of the track it is possible to read the
Polish notation for the logical connectives used. As follows:

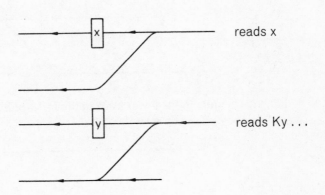

so when joined to the first sorting

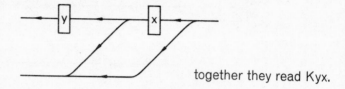

together they read Kyx.

Moving the gate to lower track at the fork introduces a negation,

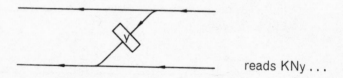

reads KNy . . .

If we now redraw the track,

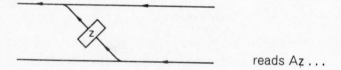

reads Az . . .

this can be joined to the first sorting as before;

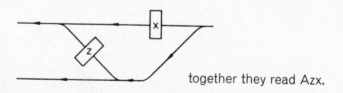

together they read Azx.

Moving the gate to the lower track at the fork again introduces a negation.

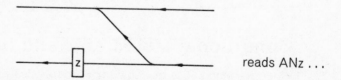

reads ANz . . .

Also we have a piece of track

which reads N . . .

When this is applied as described in the previous section (page 136),

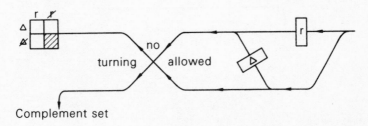

each block that arrives in the output set will be not either triangular or red, i.e. NA△r.

From an earlier discussion the reader will recall that one compartment of the Carroll diagram can be filled by a track representing a conjunctive logic statement.

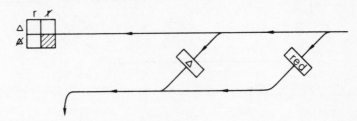

In Polish notation this will be KN△Nr.

This is a further part of De Morgan's theorem in which we have now shown that

$$NA\triangle r \; \equiv \; KN\triangle Nr$$

The reader will find it a useful exercise to find other such equivalences.

Conditional statements and notation

When we wish to use the logic tracks for implication, we need to remember that each 'if . . . then . . .' statement is equivalent to an 'either . . . or . . .' as explained earlier. So the gate necessary would be basically the A kind.

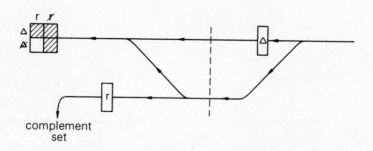

complement
set

| | ANr | | $\triangle$ | i.e. ANr$\triangle$ |
| also reads | Cr | | $\triangle$ | i.e. Cr$\triangle$ |

where C is the binary operation 'if . . . then . . .'
    The alternative track would be

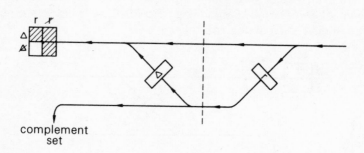

complement
set

| | A$\triangle$ | | Nr | i.e. A$\triangle$Nr |
| also reads | CN$\triangle$ | | Nr | i.e. CN$\triangle$Nr |

We have not yet considered the track necessary to select blocks for which it is true that each block is 'red if and only if triangular'.
    The layout is very ingenious in this case

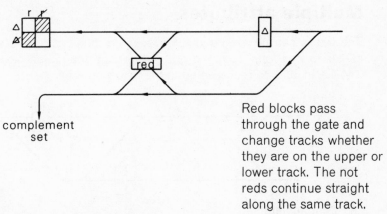

Red blocks pass through the gate and change tracks whether they are on the upper or lower track. The not reds continue straight along the same track.

It should be noted that the 'not crossover' is an important part of this gate. So we shall always read

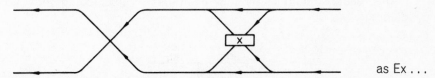

as Ex . . .

In the event that we wish to have ENx we can omit this crossover.

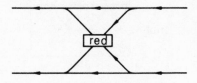

So the expression,

'Not red if and only if triangular' (i.e. ENr△)

will be represented as follows:

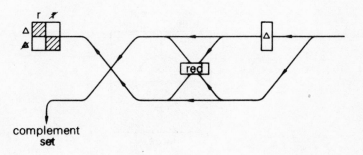

Multiple attributes

The tracks can be extended to cover more than two attributes. So the earlier expression, 'both red and either not triangular or large' (i.e. KrANΔℓ) could be represented in the following way:

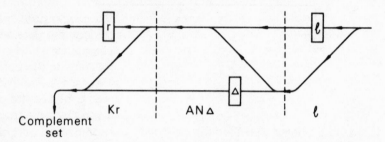

The reader should verify that the regions indicated in the Carroll diagram

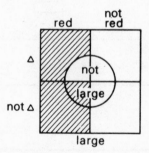

will be occupied by sets of blocks after they have passed along the track.

Another exercise that the reader might try is to draw the track and give the Polish expression which will produce blocks to fill the following regions in the Carroll diagram.

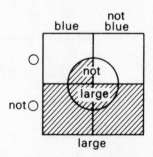

Deductions

One of the interesting consequences of developing a schematic and symbol system to represent the logic statements we have made so far, is the opportunity which they present for the process of reasoning. Since this book is intended only as an introduction, it is not possible to give more than a brief glimpse of the way in which this can be developed.

We need to remember that we can only reason from a strong condition to a weak one. For example, the statement (about a block hidden from sight) 'it is a blue circle' enables us to know for certain (i.e. deduce) two separate statements:

(a) it is blue,
   and
(b) it is a circle.

We know that these last two statements (deductions) are weaker than the initial statement (premise) since there are more blue blocks and also there are more circles than there are blue circles. On the other hand, the premise 'it is either a blue or a circle' enables us to make no deduction at all, since we cannot be certain that the block in question is blue, since it could well be a red circle, or a yellow circle.

The statement 'it is either a blue or a circle' is weaker since there are 24 blocks in a 48-piece system which satisfy the condition, of which only 16 are blue and 12 are circles.

In fact we are saying that deductions depend upon knowing that if a block is in a subset of a given set, then it is in the set itself. Hence if 'it is both a blue and a circle', the block is in the subset of blue circles contained within the set of blues and the set of circles. This is not true in the case of the block that 'is either a blue or a circle' since this determines a set which is not a subset of the blues or a subset of the circles.

Of course, this is a very simple case of deduction. To show a more complex situation let us consider two premises about a hidden block:

(a) *If* it is blue *then* it is a triangle.
(b) It is *not* a triangle.

Are we able to deduce anything about its colour? We are hoping to establish that the block belongs to a subset of a set which describes the colour of the block. We will then be able to make a deduction about the colour.

Under premise (a) the shaded regions of the Carroll diagram below will be filled:

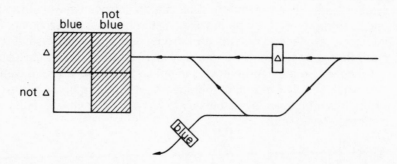

However, under premise (b) only the *two* shaded regions of the Carroll diagram will be filled:

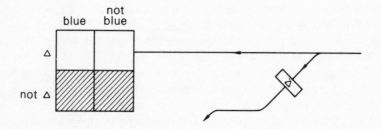

If both conditions are satisfied at the same time the block we are seeking can only be in the shaded region shown below.

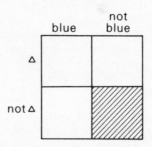

This set is a subset of the set of blocks that are not blue. Hence we can make the deduction about the hidden block, 'it is *not* blue'.

To be more formal, the premises can be written in Polish notation; a line is then drawn below them, followed by any deductions which can be made. A further line is used for any subsequent deduction. This must, of course, be a weaker condition than the first deduction. In the example given above we should write:

Premise (a) CbΔ   → If blue then Δ
Premise (b) NΔ   → not Δ

Deduction 1 KNbNΔ → both not blue and not Δ

Deduction 2 Nb   → not blue

Conclusion

Clearly there is a great deal more that can be developed from these beginnings.* The early part of the work in logic follows from the child's discussion of the objects and events he sees around him in the world. This leads to the development of language to describe the situations he explores. The later stages lead towards mathematical logic which can be developed as far and as rigorously as seems appropriate for each individual student.

---

* Professor Dienes's new *Living Mathematics* series, now (1975) in active preparation, includes useful further reading; the first three books to be published are likely to be *Relations and Functions*, *Exploring Space Around Us,* and *Sets and their Logic*. For further information, write to the Primary Editor, University of London Press Ltd, St Paul's House, 8–12 Warwick Lane, London EC4P 4AH.